A Basic English Grammar
Exercises

With Key

John Eastwood

Oxford University Press

Oxford University Press
Walton Street, Oxford OX2 6DP

Oxford   New York   Toronto
Delhi   Bombay   Calcutta   Madras   Karachi
Petaling Jaya   Singapore   Hong Kong   Tokyo
Nairobi   Dar es Salaam   Cape Town
Melbourne   Auckland

and associated companies in
Beirut   Berlin   Ibadan   Nicosia

OXFORD is a trade mark of Oxford University Press.

ISBN 0 19 432941 0

First published 1984
Fifth impression 1986

The publishers thank Barnabys Picture Library for
permission to reproduce photographs. The location
photographs are by Rosie Potter and Terry Williams.

Illustrations by Alex Brychta, Roy Ingram, Peter Joyce,
Mike Ogden and Alan Suttie.

Filmset in Helvetica by Filmtype Services Limited,
Scarborough, North Yorkshire.

Printed in Yugoslavia

Contents

Introduction

This book contains exercises giving practice in the main grammatical points covered in *A Basic English Grammar*. The exercises are suitable for students up to an intermediate level.

Each exercise consists of a controlled practice followed by a more open-ended Activity. The controlled practice is the main part of each exercise. It may be gap-filling, sentence construction etc. and is always set in an overall context. It can be done orally and/or in writing in class or for homework. The Activity should be done in class. It may involve pair or group work, discussion, a game, problem-solving etc. and is designed to encourage a more communicative use of the grammar being practised. It is of course possible to do only the main part of the exercise and to leave out the Activity.

At the head of each exercise is a reference to the section or sections of *A Basic English Grammar* (BEG) which contain the grammar to be practised. These sections can be consulted as necessary. Some exercises deal with one particular grammatical point, while others cover wider topics, such as 'Talking about the past', which takes up a whole chapter of *A Basic English Grammar*. The book provides opportunities to compare and contrast grammatical forms as well as to practise some points individually.

This book is published in two editions, one with a Key (pages 105–124) and one without. The Key contains the answers to all the items in the main part of each exercise, but it does not cover the Activities.

1 (BEG 1.1–1.6)

Word order

Four men have kidnapped the son of a very rich family. The men are going to send a letter to the family, and they have cut these words out of a newspaper. Put the words in the correct order.

Example

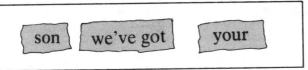

| son | we've got | your |

We've got your son.

Activity

Cut a sentence out of an English newspaper or magazine. Then cut the sentence into separate words or phrases and ask a partner to put them in the correct order.

If you haven't got an English newspaper, write a sentence on a piece of paper and then cut it up. You can copy the sentence from an English book.

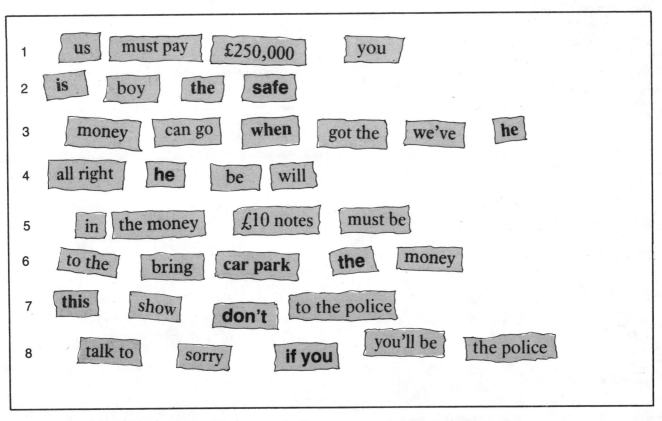

1 | us | must pay | £250,000 | you |

2 | is | boy | the | safe |

3 | money | can go | when | got the | we've | he |

4 | all right | he | be | will |

5 | in | the money | £10 notes | must be |

6 | to the | bring | car park | the | money |

7 | this | show | don't | to the police |

8 | talk to | sorry | if you | you'll be | the police |

5

2 (BEG 2.1)

The present tense of be

It's the Drama Club tonight, but not everyone has arrived yet. Complete the dialogue using present tense forms of *be*. Some forms are positive (e.g. *is*) and some negative (e.g. *isn't*); some are full forms (e.g. *are*) and some short forms (e.g. *'re*).

Jane ... we all here now?
Mark Where ... Tom? He ... here.
Helen Oh, he ... very well. He ... in bed.
Lynn Oh, dear. Poor Tom. And Sarah ... here.
Sarah Oh, yes, I ....
Jane Oh, there you ..., over in the corner. Sorry, Sarah.
Mark Angela ... late. Or ... she ill, too?
Helen No, she ... ill.
Lynn Peter and Sue ... here.
Jane Yes, they .... They ... in the kitchen.
Angela Hello, everybody. ... I late?
Jane Yes, you ....
Angela Oh, I ... sorry.
Jane Tell Peter and Sue to come, Mark.
Peter It ... all right. Here we ....
Jane Good. Now we ... ready to start.

Activity

One student thinks of a famous living person or a group of people such as a pop group. Ask questions to find out who the person is, e.g. *Is it one person? Is it a man? Is he European? Are they a sports team? Is she Queen Elizabeth?*

3 (BEG 2.1; 2.2)

The present tense of be and have

Mr and Mrs Johnson want to sell their house. Say things about the house using a form of *be* or *have*.

Examples

house – 200 years old.
The house is 200 years old.

all rooms – central heating.
All the rooms have central heating.

1 garden – lovely
2 views to the north and east – beautiful
3 house – six bedrooms
4 rooms – large
5 downstairs rooms – carpets
6 sitting room – lovely old fireplace
7 kitchen – plenty of cupboards
8 garage – big enough for three cars

Activity

Write a short description of the house or flat you live in.

The present tense of **have got**

It's the first week of January. There are sales at the big department stores, and you can buy some things very cheaply. What have these people got?

Examples

He's got a shirt.

They've got some chairs.

Activity A

Find some more pictures. Look through a magazine or a textbook and talk to a partner about the things people have got. If you don't know the word in English, ask your teacher.

Activity B

Ask your partner what he/she has got at home. Ask e.g. *Have you got a camera? Have you got a computer? Have you got a bicycle?* Then tell your partner what you've got.

5 (BEG 2.3)

The present continuous tense

These people are playing a game. They are miming things. You have to say what they are doing. These phrases will help you: *brush his/her teeth, carry something, climb a ladder, comb his/her hair, eat an apple, play cards, read the newspaper, take a photo, wash his/her hands.*

Example

She's taking a photo.

Activity A

Play the miming game. One student mimes an action, and the others ask *Are you sweeping the floor? Are you writing something?* etc.

Activity B

Talk about these photos and say what the people in them are doing.

6 (BEG 2.4)

The simple present tense (positive statements)

Complete this newspaper story about Lord Stonebury. Put in the correct simple present form of these verbs: go (× 4), have (× 3), live (× 2), get, meet, own, play, read, spend, talk.

LORD STONEBURY TELLS ALL!

from an interview by our reporter Tim Bennett, and only in the Daily Talk

Lord Stonebury is twenty-eight years old. He … in Belgravia in London's West End. He's very rich, and he … the company Office Blocks International. Every morning the young Lord … breakfast in bed and … the newspapers. He … up at ten o'clock and usually … for a walk in Hyde Park. He … lunch at his club. He sometimes … the Directors of OBI, and they … about the company's plans.

In the afternoon Lord Stonebury and his friends sometimes … golf. Then they … a few drinks. Or sometimes he and a girl-friend … for a drive in his sports car.

After dinner Lord Stonebury … to a night club or a casino with one of his girl-friends. They … home at about two o'clock.

In the winter the young Lord … in Monte Carlo. And he … his summer holidays in the West Indies.

Activity

Write the story of a typical day in your life.

7 (BEG 2.4)

The simple present tense (positive and negative statements)

Amanda hasn't got a boy-friend. The Find-a-Friend Club wants to help her. Look at Amanda's answers to the club's questionnaire and write sentences about her.

Examples

Amanda reads books.
She doesn't watch a lot of television.

Put a tick in the box.

Do you …	Yes	No
read books?	✓	
watch a lot of television?		✓
play computer games?		✓
like music?	✓	
often visit people?	✓	
like sport?		✓
go swimming?		✓
like animals?		✓
go for walks?	✓	
often go out in the evenings?		✓

Activity

You are writing a letter to the Find-a-Friend Club. Write a paragraph saying what you like and what you do in your spare time.

8 (BEG 2.4)

The simple present tense (questions)

Tim Bennett is interviewing Brenda Bagg. Brenda writes love stories, and millions of people read her books. Complete Tim's questions by putting in the missing words.

Tim Brenda, where … your ideas for all your stories?
Brenda Where do I get my ideas? That's hard to say. They just come to me.
Tim … a long time to write a book?
Brenda No, it doesn't take long. I write one in about two weeks.
Tim Really? That's very quick. … every day?
Brenda Yes, I write every day.
Tim And … ?
Brenda Oh, I work here in the sitting-room.
Tim … your stories?
Brenda No, I don't — my secretary types them.
Tim … your husband … your stories?
Brenda No, he doesn't. He hates them.
Tim … your husband … , Brenda?
Brenda Oh, he doesn't work. He hasn't got a job. My stories bring us lots of money, you know.
Tim … so many people … your books, Brenda?
Brenda I think they read them because I tell a good story. Everyone likes a good story, you know.

Activity

Take the role of a famous person who you know something about. Your partner interviews you and asks about your daily life.

9 (BEG 2.1; 2.2; 2.4)

The present tense of **be** and **have**; the simple present tense

This paragraph is from a book about British towns. It's about a town called Milchester. Complete the paragrah by putting in present tense forms of *be* and *have* and the simple present tense of *bring, live* and *work*.

Milchester … a lovely old town on the River Swenley. The famous castle … lots of tourists to the town. The old streets near the castle … many interesting little shops, and there … a very good museum. The town also … a theatre and a cinema. 27,000 people … in Milchester, and quite a few of them … at the new computer factory. Other industries … paper-making and chocolate.

Activity

Write a short description of a town that you know well.

Present continuous or simple present?

It's a holiday today. The people below aren't working. Say what they do in their jobs and what they're doing at the moment. Use these verbs in the present continuous: *eat, jog, listen, play, read, ride, swim, wash, watch.*

RAY, WINDOW CLEANER

Example

Ray cleans windows. He's listening to the radio at the moment.

BRIAN, HOUSE BUILDER

ALICE, MUSIC TEACHER

MAUREEN AND JACKIE, DRESSMAKERS

ALAN, LORRY DRIVER

STEPHEN, GOLFER

JESSICA, NEWSREADER

TONY AND ROGER, CAR SALESMEN

MIRANDA, PHOTOGRAPHER

Activity

Make sentences about the people in these photos. Use both the present continuous and simple present tenses.

11 (BEG 2.5; 2.6)

Present continuous or simple present?

Complete this postcard using the correct form of the verbs on the right.

Greetings from Wales! Ben and I ...
something different this year. We're at the
North Wales Activity Centre. People ...
here every summer to learn more about
their hobbies and interests. I ...
photography and tennis this week and
Ben ... about computers. We ... up at half
past eight every morning and ... lessons
from ten to half past twelve. We ... lunch
at one, and then there are more lessons.
So it's hard work. But I ... it here. We ... a
super time. It's half past seven in the
evening now, and we ... out on the grass
in front of the Centre. The weather is
good. See you soon.

do

come

do

learn, get
do
have

like, have

sit

Love,

Kate

Activity

Write a postcard to an English friend from the place where you last went on holiday. Say what you do every day on holiday and what you are doing at the moment.

12 (BEG 3.1)

The past tense of **be**

Helen and David are talking about a barbecue. (At a barbecue people cook meat over a fire. They cook and eat the meal outside.) Complete the dialogue. Use *was, wasn't, were* or *weren't*.

Helen I hear there ... a barbecue at the college last Saturday. ... you there?
David Yes, I .... Where ... you?
Helen Oh, I ... here on Saturday. I ... in London.
David That's a pity. It ... a very good barbecue. The food ... great.
Helen What ... the weather like here?
David Oh, we ... very lucky with the weather. It ... nice and warm.
Helen ... there a lot of people there?
David Yes, lots. Lynn ... there, though. She ... very well.
Helen What about Mark and Jane?
David Oh, they ... still on holiday last Saturday, so they ... at the barbecue. But all the others ... there.

Activity

One student imagines that he/she was in a certain place yesterday evening, e.g. at a concert, in a plane. Ask questions to find out where the person was, e.g. *Were you in hospital? Were you at a disco?*

13 (BEG 3.1; 3.2)

The past tense of **be** and **have**

A number of people saw a monster in the sea on the south coast of England. One of them was Henry. He's talking to reporters about it. Put in *was, wasn't, were, weren't, had* or *didn't have*.

Reporter What happened? Where … you? And where … the monster?
Henry I … here on the beach. I saw the monster in the water. Then it swam out to sea. It … a great shock. It … very nice, I can tell you.
Reporter What … the monster like?
Henry Big. It … a very large animal. It … a large body, but it … a small head. Its eyes … blue and round. It … teeth, but they … very big. It … any ears.
Reporter Did you take a photo of it?
Henry I … my camera with me, I'm afraid. And it … very quick. It all happened in a moment.

Activity

Imagine that you were out in the country one evening and you saw a spaceship land and two Martians get out. Your partner is a reporter interviewing you about it.

14 (BEG 3.3)

The simple past tense (positive statements)

Find the correct action for each person.

Examples

Copernicus studied the planets.
Shakespeare wrote plays.

People	Actions
Copernicus	going to the moon
Shakespeare	inventing the electric light
Picasso	making clothes
Billie-Jean King	painting pictures
Neil Armstrong	playing tennis
Marco Polo	sailing to America
Martin Luther King	studying the planets
Christian Dior	travelling to China
Columbus	working for Black people's rights
Edison	writing plays

Activity

Say what these people did.

Elvis Presley
Agatha Christie
Henry Ford
Alfred Hitchcock
Marconi

The simple past tense
(positive statements)

You saw this robbery take place yesterday evening.

Tell the police what you saw. Put in the simple past forms of the verbs on the right.

1 A car … outside the shop, and two men … out. — *stop* / *get*
2 They … masks on. — *have*
3 One of them … a brick in his hand. — *hold*
4 He … the brick at the window and … it. — *throw* / *smash*
5 One man … the coats from the window, and the other … them in the back of the car. — *take* / *put*
6 It all … very quickly. People just … and … . — *happen* / *stand, watch*
7 The men … into the car and … away. — *jump, drive*
8 I … to a phone box and … the police. — *run, call*

Activity

Imagine that you were in a bank one day and you saw a bank raid take place. The police want to know what you saw. Write the story of what happened.

16 (BEG 3.3)

The simple past tense (positive and negative statements)

Bob had a lot of jobs to do last weekend. He didn't have time to do all of them. Which ones did he do?

Examples

He washed the car.
He didn't buy a new battery for the car.

<u>Weekend</u>

wash car ✓
buy new battery for car
repair broken window
book holiday
write to bank ✓
phone sports club
pay electricity bill ✓
tidy garage ✓
paint gate
clean windows

Activity

Write down five things you did last weekend. (They needn't just be jobs.) Compare your list with your partner's. Say if you did the same things or not.

17 (BEG 3.3)

The simple past tense (questions)

Melinda Burns is a famous film star. Two weeks ago she suddenly disappeared, and no one knew where she was. The police looked everywhere for her. Yesterday she arrived home, and now she is speaking to reporters for the first time. Read what the reporters are thinking and ask their questions.

Examples

(She went somewhere. Where?)
Where did you go?

(Perhaps someone kidnapped her.)
Did someone kidnap you?

1 (She disappeared. Why?)
2 (Perhaps she left the country.)
3 (She travelled. How?)
4 (Perhaps her friends hid her.)
5 (She did something in all that time. What?)
6 (Perhaps she read the stories about her in the newspapers.)
7 (She came home. Why?)
8 (Perhaps her husband found her.)

Activity

You work for a magazine called 'Holiday'. You are interviewing people. Ask your partner about his/her last holiday. Find out all the details.

The present perfect tense

A month ago the members of the Parkway Sports and Social Club decided to clean and decorate their club. The club hasn't got much money, so the members have done the work in their spare time. They've just finished now. Say what they have done.

Examples

(The windows needed painting.)
Sue and Peter have painted the windows.

(The members decided to plant a tree.)
Jane has planted a tree.

1 (The fence needed repairing.)
2 (The club room needed decorating.)
3 (They decided to buy some new curtains.)
4 (The cups needed polishing.)
5 (The minibus needed servicing.)
6 (They decided to lay a new carpet in the bar.)
7 (The kitchen needed cleaning out.)
8 (They decided to put up some more shelves.)

Activity

Four students leave the room and the rest of you decide to change four things in the room, e.g. to open a window, to take down a poster, to put some books on top of the cupboard or to move the waste bin. The four students come back and have a good look round. They ask e.g. *Have your turned that desk round? Have you rubbed out the sentence on the board?* and you answer *Yes, we have* or *No, we haven't.*

19 (BEG 3.5)

Present perfect or simple past?

James Delaney is the most famous sportsman in Britain. He's quite old now, but he's done lots of exciting things in his life. Here are some photos in a magazine article about him. Say what James has done and when he did it.

Examples
He's played tennis at Wimbledon. He played tennis there in 1948.
He's taken part in the Olympic Games. He took part (in them) in 1956.

Activity

Have *you* done any exciting or interesting things? Write down one or two. Find out what other people in your class have done.

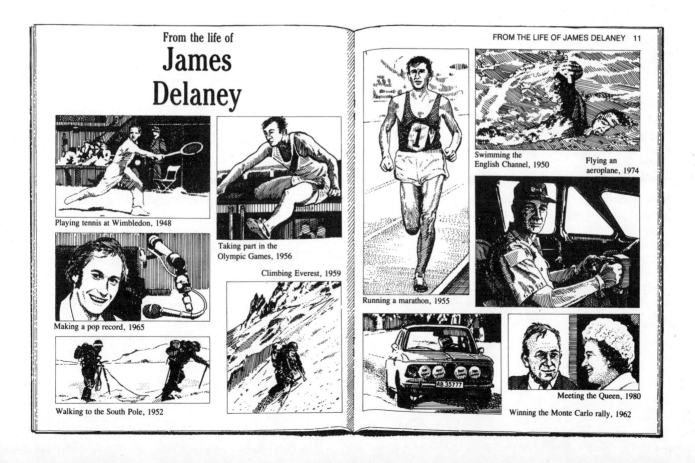

From the life of
James
Delaney

Playing tennis at Wimbledon, 1948

Making a pop record, 1965

Walking to the South Pole, 1952

Taking part in the Olympic Games, 1956

Climbing Everest, 1959

FROM THE LIFE OF JAMES DELANEY 11

Swimming the English Channel, 1950

Flying an aeroplane, 1974

Running a marathon, 1955

Meeting the Queen, 1980

Winning the Monte Carlo rally, 1962

20 (BEG 3.5)

Present perfect or simple past?

Complete this conversation by putting the verbs in brackets into the present perfect or simple past.

Rachel Hello, Bob.
Bob Hello. I (not see) you for a long time.
Rachel I (see) you in town two or three weeks ago, but you (not see) me. I (be) on a bus.
Bob Well, how are things? Are you still living over the shop?
Rachel No, I (move) now. I (find) a super flat just before I went on holiday. I (be) there three months.
Bob … you (pass) your driving test yet?
Rachel Yes, I have. I (pass) in October. I (not buy) a car yet, though. But what about you, Bob? … anything exciting (happen) to you lately?
Bob No, not really. My mother (not be) very well for a few months now.
Rachel Oh, dear. I'm sorry to hear that.
Bob And my brother's out of work.
Rachel … he (leave) school in the summer, then?
Bob Yes. He (not do) very well in his exams and he (not find) a job yet.
Rachel Are you still working at Scott's?
Bob Yes. They … just (give) me a pay rise.
Rachel Well, that's one piece of good news.

Activity

Imagine that you are meeting an old friend who you haven't seen for about a year. Write down three or four items of news about yourself that you can tell your friend.

21 (BEG 3.6)

The past perfect tense

Decide the order in which these things happened. Then write two sentences using *after* and the past perfect.

Example

The prisoner ran across the yard.
He jumped out of the window.
He climbed over the wall.

After the prisoner had jumped out of the window, he ran across the yard.
After he had run across the yard, he climbed over the wall.

1 The bank clerk gave it to me.
   She looked at my cheque.
   She counted out the money.

2 The tourists got out of the coach.
   They got back in the coach.
   They took photos.

3 The reporter wrote a report on the accident.
   She interviewed the people there.
   She went to the scene of the accident.

4 The mechanic put a new tyre on.
   He put the wheel back on.
   He took the wheel off the car.

Activity

Write a paragraph describing how you carried out a job such as wrapping a parcel and posting it. (You can use these words: *parcel, paper, wrap, stick, tape, tie, string, post office, assistant, weigh, pay, stamp*). Try to think of a job that you did recently.

22 (BEG 3.7)

The past continuous tense

Mr Pratt has a lot of dreams. He's telling a psychiatrist about them. How does Mr Pratt describe his dreams? Look at the pictures and the psychiatrist's notes.

Examples

I was driving a car when a wheel came off. *The Queen walked in when we were eating breakfast.*

drives car – wheel comes off
eat breakfast – Queen comes in
walks across bridge – meets tiger
roof falls in – watch television
climbs stairs – sees ghost
looks into mirror – it breaks
wind blows him over cliff – walks along
path
lie on beach – elephant comes out of sea
digs garden – finds dead body

Activity A
Last night Mr Pratt had these two dreams. How do you think he described them?

Activity B
Have you had any interesting or amusing dreams? Can you describe them?

23 (BEG 3.8)

The present perfect continuous tense

Twelve students live in a big old house. Today they're all helping to clean it and tidy it up. Read the conversation and say how long they've been doing their jobs. Use a phrase with *for*.

Example

Gary has been throwing away rubbish for an hour and a half.

Adam What are you doing, Gary?
Gary Throwing away rubbish. I started at half past ten, and it's twelve o'clock now, look.
Melanie I'm washing up. I've been doing it since half past eleven.
Adam Sadie and I are tidying up. We started at half past ten.
Lisa Has anyone seen a bucket? I've been looking for one since ten to twelve.
Gary I think Alison and Jason had a bucket. They're working in the garden. They've been there since nine o'clock.
Lisa What's Don doing?
Adam He's cleaning the stairs. He's been doing that since Melanie started washing up.
Emma And I'm repairing this toaster. I started at eleven o'clock, but it still won't work.
Adam Trevor's mending the door bell. He began the job at about twenty to twelve.
Melanie Daniel and Rebecca are brushing carpets. They started at ten.
Gary Let's all go out and have some lunch soon.
Adam Good idea.

Activity

Find out who in your class has been living in the same house or flat the longest.

24 (BEG 3.1–3.9)

Talking about the past

Complete this newspaper article by putting each verb in brackets into the correct past or perfect tense. (Sometimes there is more than one correct answer.)

UNITED WANT SIMMONDS

Manchester United manager Brian Price (go) to Turin for talks with the Juventus club about Wayne Simmonds. Simmonds (join) Juventus a year ago, and he (score) 18 goals for them. Last autumn he (score) almost every week, but he (not play) well recently. English fans would welcome his return, and yesterday everyone at United (talk) about Simmonds. In fact, the club (wait) for some time now for a chance to talk to the player.

At the moment Simmonds is England's greatest footballer, although he (be) in the game for only two years. He (play) amateur football for Mendip Athletic when Bristol City (invite) him to join them. When Arsenal (buy) Simmonds for £750,000, he (spend) only six months with the Bristol club, but he (already play) twice for England Under-21s. Simmonds quickly (become) a big star, and he (now play) five games for the full England team, although he (play) only one game for them since he (leave) Arsenal for Juventus.

Activity

Write a short paragraph about a famous living person summarizing his/her career so far.

25 (BEG 3.1–3.10)

Talking about the past

A lawyer has made some notes about a traffic accident. Complete them by putting each verb in brackets into the correct past or perfect tense. (Sometimes there is more than one correct answer.)

Traffic accident: Mr Keith Johnson, 44 Grange Rd, Milchester

1 The accident (happen) at 10.47 pm on October 23rd at the corner of Compton St and Brooks Rd, Milchester.
2 Mr and Mrs Johnson (be) on their way home. Mr Johnson (drive).
3 The couple (visit) friends. They (drink), but Mr Johnson (have) only one small whisky. He (finish) this drink at 10.15 pm.
4 It (not rain) at the time, but it (rain) shortly before, and the roads (be) wet.
5 At 10.47 pm Mr Richard Hunter (cycle) north along Brooks Rd. He (have) his lights on.
6 Mr Johnson (not stop) at the 'Stop' sign. As he (turn) into Brooks Rd, he (hit) Mr Hunter and (knock) him off his bike.
7 Mr Hunter (be) not badly hurt, but his bike (be) damaged. Mr Johnson (stop) and (report) the accident.
8 Mr Johnson (drive) for twenty years now. He (not have) an accident before.

Activity

Tell your partner about an accident that once happened to you or one that you saw. It can be a road accident or an accident at work or in the home.

26 (BEG 3.1–3.11)

Talking about the past

Mrs Vincent is a hundred years old. She's talking to a reporter. Complete their conversation by putting the verbs in brackets into the correct tense. You can use the simple past, the present perfect, the present perfect continuous or *used to*. (Sometimes there is more than one correct answer.)

Reporter How long … you (live) in this house, Mrs Vincent?
Mrs Vincent I (live) here for seventy-five years now.
Reporter And how long is it since your husband (die)?
Mrs Vincent Oh, he (be) dead for forty years. Yes, he (die) a long time ago. I (be) alone since then. It (be) a long time.
Reporter And where … you (live) before you (come) here?
Mrs Vincent Well, before we (get) married I (live) with my parents in William Street. They (knock) the house down now. I (only live) in two houses all my life.
Reporter I expect you (see) a lot of changes in all that time.
Mrs Vincent Oh, yes. Milchester (be) very quiet in my young days. And it (not be) as big as it is today. I (go) for picnics on Long Hill with my brothers and sisters. Now they (build) houses there.
Reporter … you (enjoy) life in those days?
Mrs Vincent Oh, yes. We (have) a wonderful time. People (be) a lot friendlier in those days. We (do) things together. Nowadays people just sit at home and watch television, don't they?

Activity

Write three or four sentences about *your* childhood and the place where you lived then. Ask a partner about his/her childhood.

27 (BEG 4.1)

will

There's a programme about the future on television tonight. Professor Joseph T. Bloomenberg is saying what the world will be like in fifty years' time. Look at the Professor's notes and write down what he says.

Examples

People will live longer.
There will be more people in the world.

```
people living longer
more people in the world
robots doing all the hard work
not so many jobs
people having more free time
the weather colder
not very much oil
fish farms under the sea
people flying to other planets
people not very happy
```

Activity

Write a few sentences saying what you think the world will be like in fifty years' time.

28 (BEG 4.3)

be going to

The pupils in Class 6F at Parkside School are all seventeen or eighteen years old. Most of them are going to leave school soon. Read the information about them and then say what they're going to do. Choose the correct phrase from the box below.

Example

Andrew is interested in machines.
Andrew is going to study engineering.

1 Neil wants to be out in the fresh air.
2 Michelle and Kevin are interested in computers.
3 Sharon has already learnt to drive.
4 Simon is good with numbers.
5 Nick and Julie need to take their exams again.
6 Adrian's parents have their own company.
7 Tina would like to work with people.
8 Ian and Jeremy want to get away for a while.

```
become a taxi driver
do electronics
hitch-hike round the world
look for an outdoor job
stay at school another year
study engineering
take a course in banking
train to be a social worker
work for the family business
```

Activity A

If you're still at school or college, say what you're going to do in the future.

Activity B

Say what you're going to do next weekend. Write three or four sentences.

will and **be going to**

Bymore's is a big department store. It's quite an old store now. The management of Bymore's have decided to modernize the store. The picture shows what they have decided to do. The manager of the store is explaining what they are going to do and what the result will be. Write down what the manager says.

Example

We're going to have a computer. It'll tell us what people are buying.

1 We're going to put in …. They'll …
2 … employ …
3 … put in … .
4 … play …
5 … have …
6 … have … … be able …

Ex computer to tell us what people are buying

1 new escalators to move people around more quickly

5 televisions to inform customers about things in the store

4 music to produce the right atmosphere

2 more assistants to help our customers

3 cameras to stop people stealing things

SPORTS

6 children's room for parents to leave their children

Activity

Imagine that you are in charge of your school or college. Discuss with the rest of the class what changes you would like to make in the building. You must make definite decisions, and you have plenty of money to spend. Write down your decisions and say what the results will be.

30 (BEG 4.1–4.3)

will, shall and be going to

Graham and his family are going to move from
London to Alaska. Janet is asking Graham about the
move. Put in *'ll, will, won't, shall, shan't* or a form of
be going to. (Sometimes there is more than one
correct answer.)

Janet Someone told me you and the family … go
and live in Alaska. Is it true?
Graham Yes, it is. I … work for a building company.
Janet That … be interesting.
Graham I hope so. It … be something different. It …
certainly be a lot colder than London.
Janet When … you … leave?
Graham On the tenth of next month. We … be there
in three weeks.
Janet Oh, so it … be long now. Jerry and I … be sad
to see you go.
Graham Oh, we … be back some time. We … be
there for ever. And you can always come to Alaska
and see us.
Janet Well, that isn't a bad idea. We … visit my
sister in Vancouver next summer.
Graham Oh, that's great. We … see you next
summer then.

Activity

Imagine that Janet and Graham live in Birmingham,
and Graham, who is single, has got a new job with an
oil company in Saudi Arabia starting in two weeks.
Rewrite the conversation changing the details where
necessary. Then practise the conversation with a
partner.

31 (BEG 4.5; 4.6)

The present continuous and simple present tenses with a future meaning

Charles Dearborn is the managing director of
Ramplus Computers, an international company with
its main offices in London. Mr Dearborn has a busy
life. Describe his schedule for next week. For the
times of arrival and departure use the simple present
form. To describe the other arrangements use the
present continuous form of these verbs: *speak, visit,
open, meet, have, go.*

Example

*On Monday he leaves London at 9.30 and arrives in
Madrid at 12.40. He is speaking at an international
conference.*

Monday	London 9.30 Madrid 12.40
	International conference
Tuesday	Madrid 7.40 Athens 13.55
	Ramplus offices
Wednesday	Athens 8.15 Milan 12.35
	New Ramplus factory
Thursday	Milan 10.10 Strasbourg 11.15
	President of the Common Market
Friday	Strasbourg 10.45 The Hague 11.40
	Discussions with the Dutch Minister of Technology
Saturday	The Hague 9.30 Stockholm 12.25
	Computer show

Activity

Imagine you are the head of a big international
company. You have just met your partner at a party,
and you are telling him/her about a three-day
business trip you are making next week. Think of
some interesting places and important things to do
and tell your partner about them.

32 (BEG 4.5; 4.8)

The present continuous tense with a future meaning; **be to**

These newspaper headlines are all about things in the future. Write the headlines as full sentences using the present continuous tense or *be to*. Sometimes you also need to put in *the, a* or *some*.

Examples

GAS PRICES GOING UP IN NOVEMBER
Gas prices are going up in November.

NEW LONDON CONFERENCE CENTRE TO OPEN SOON
A new London conference centre is to open soon.

1 WORLD LEADERS TO MEET NEXT MONTH
2 DOCK STRIKE STARTING TOMORROW
3 PRIME MINISTER TO VISIT GREECE IN AUGUST
4 QUEEN LEAVING FOR AUSTRALIA TOMORROW
5 CHINESE TOURISTS ARRIVING IN BRITAIN NEXT SATURDAY
6 SHOE FACTORY TO CLOSE
7 EUROPEAN GAMES TO TAKE PLACE NEXT YEAR
8 THREE NEW PLAYERS JOINING LIVERPOOL

Activity

Try to think of news stories that you have heard recently about things arranged to happen in the future. Write two sentences like those in the exercises but about real events.

33 (BEG 4,1; 4,7; 4,10)

will, will be + -ing form and **will have** + -ed form

Madame Zaza is a fortune teller. She's telling Julie what her life will be like. Complete the sentences using *will, will be* or *will have* and a form of the verb in brackets.

1 You (be) on holiday soon. In two weeks from now you (lie) on a beach.
2 You (have) a good life, and you (live) a long time.
3 Your personality is changing all the time. In ten years time you (change) completely.
4 At some time in your life you (have) a bad accident, but you (not die).
5 You (marry) when you are twenty-three.
6 In twenty years from now you (live) on the other side of the world. By that time you (leave) your husband.
7 You (be) rich. When you are thirty-five, you (already make) a lot of money.
8 At this time of your life you (work) very hard. Your life (be) very exciting.

Activity

Imagine you are visiting Madame Zaza. Write three predictions that you would like to hear from her. Use *will, will be* and *will have.*

34 (BEG 4,1–4.7)

Talking about the future

Sue and Kate are discussing their holiday plans. Complete their conversation using *will, 'll, won't, shall* or *be going to* with the verbs in brackets, or use a present tense form of the verb. (Usually there is more than one correct answer.)

Sue Where … you and Ben (go) for your holidays, Kate?

Kate Morocco. We (spend) ten days in Agadir.

Sue Oh, that (be) nice. When … you (go)?

Kate On Friday night. Our plane (leave) at seven, and we (arrive) at four in the morning.

Sue You (need) a holiday after that.

Kate Oh, I don't mind night flights. Anyway, we (enjoy) the sunshine this time next week.

Sue … you (stay) in a hotel?

Kate Yes, a big hotel not far from the beach.

Sue Our holiday (not be) until next month. Jerry and I (tour) Scotland in the car, we've decided. We (do) some walking, too. The weather (not be) like Agadir, of course.

Kate How long … you (go) for?

Sue Two weeks. We haven't been to Scotland before, so it (be) something different.

Kate … you (take) your caravan?

Sue No, we don't want to take the caravan. We (have to) find hotels to stay in as we go.

Kate Well, we (be) back from Morocco before you go.

Sue Have a nice time, Kate.

Activity

Discuss your holiday plans with other people in your class.

35 (BEG 5.1)

be, have and do used as auxiliary verbs

A reporter has written a newspaper article about a boy who writes computer games programmes. Put in *is, are, was, were, has, have, had, do, does* or *did*. Sometimes you need a negative form with *n't*.

COMPUTER WONDER-BOY

Mr and Mrs Stokes … sitting in the garden of their Bristol home when I arrived to interview them and their fourteen-year-old son Carl. But Carl … working upstairs. 'He … often leave his room,' his mother explained.

At the moment Carl … working on a programme for a new computer game. Computers … become his whole life. In the last year Carl … earned over £25,000 from writing programmes. A lot of other people … trying to do the same nowadays, but not many of them … done as well as Carl.

'When … he buy the computer?' I wondered. 'We bought it for him eighteen months ago for his birthday,' said Mr Stokes. 'We … know what we … doing. Our son … changed. Eighteen months ago he … seen a computer. Now he … talk about anything else. And we … understand a thing about computers.' 'And … you think it's good for him?' was my next question. 'No, we … . We worry about him,' said Mrs Stokes. 'He … have any other interests now. And he … done any work for his school exams. It's often quite a job to make him go to school at all.'

Carl's parents … understand computers, but Carl certainly … . 'I love computers,' he said. 'I soon got tired of playing games, though. I like writing programmes much better. I've got three computers now. I bought two more. I … earn much at first, but now I … . My parents make me put most of it in the bank.'

it + be and there + be

Say what the weather forecast is for tomorrow. Start each sentence with *it* or *there*.

Example

North-east: Cold. A little snow.
It'll be cold.
There'll be a little snow.

Weather forecast

North-east: Cold. A little snow.
North-west: Wet. Strong winds.
Midlands: Dry most of the time. Windy.
South-east: Some rain in places. Sunny at times.
South-west: Warm. Some sunshine.

Activity

Write one or more sentences describing the weather where you are. Use *It's* … and *There's* …

Activity

Write a similar short article about a twelve-year-old girl from Coventry called Kerry Pike who writes and sings pop songs and plays the guitar. She earns a lot of money from records and concerts.

37 (BEG 5.5)

The normal verb **have**

It's lunch time. Mike is sitting in the canteen. Paul has just joined him. Complete the conversation using a form of *have*, e.g. *had, are having*. You may need to use negative or question forms.

Paul Hello, Mike. … you … a nice time in France?
Mike Hello, Paul. Yes, we did, thanks. We … very good weather, but we still … a good time.
Paul … you already … your lunch?
Mike Yes, I was early today. And I only … a sandwich.
Paul You can … one of my sausages if you like.
Mike No, thanks. I … only … light lunches this week. I'm trying to lose weight.
Paul You haven't got anything to worry about.
Mike You're going camping in Wales next week, aren't you?
Paul That's right.
Mike I hope you … nice weather.
Paul So do I. Did you know Mark and Jane are in Benidorm at the moment? We … a postcard from them on Friday. They say they … a marvellous time.
Mike I took some photos in France. You can … a look at them some time if you like.
Paul Okay.
Mike Come round to our house tonight, and we can … a talk.

Activity

Act out the conversation with a partner. Then talk to your partner about *your* last holiday.

38 (BEG 7.2)

could and **be able to**

Six weeks ago a man and his wife were flying over the jungle when their plane came down in the trees. Last week their bodies were found about twenty miles from where the plane crashed. The woman had written a diary. Read the diary below and say what happened to the two people. Use *could, couldn't* and *was/were able to*.

Example

Thursday
We were able to climb down from the plane. We couldn't think clearly because we were so shocked.

Thursday	Climbed down from plane. Too shocked to think clearly.
Friday	Too hot to sleep. Heard the noise of insects all night.
Saturday	Got water from a stream. Saw some smoke from the south.
Sunday	Too wet to travel. Kept dry.
Monday	Walked several miles along the bank of a river. River too wide to cross.
Tuesday	Killed and ate a monkey. Heard a plane somewhere above us.
Wednesday	Both too ill to walk. Slept for several hours.

Activity

The bodies of the two people were found in a cave. The diary and a bottle half full of water were lying on the ground about fifty metres from the cave. What do you think happened after the woman stopped writing the diary?

can, could and be able to

The Psycho-Clinic in London helps people with their problems. Below is an advertisement for the clinic. Complete the sentences using *can, could, was/were able to, 'll be able to* or their negative forms. (Sometimes more than one answer is correct.)

Activity

Imagine that you were once a very shy person. You didn't like meeting people and talking to them. Then you went to Psycho-Clinic. Write a few sentences about what the clinic has done for you.

PSYCHO-CLINIC
The answer to your problems

Rosemary, Manchester

Psycho-Clinic is wonderful. My problem was that I . . . fly. I was afraid of aeroplanes. As soon as my course was over, I . . . take a flight to the Canary Islands! I had a super holiday. Now I . . . fly where I like. Next summer I . . . go to the West Indies. (I . . . do that every year because I haven't enough money.) I . . . thank Psycho-Clinic enough.

Bernard, Southampton

Now at last I . . . stand up in front of a group of people! From now on my life will be different. I . . . do my job much better in future. I often have to give talks to sales people at work. I just . . . avoid it. In the old days I . . . sleep for a week before a talk. I . . . hardly do my work. But now I . . . give a talk without feeling too nervous. Last week I . . . get a good night's sleep before talking to a group of twenty people the next day. It's marvellous!

Margaret, Cornwall

Yesterday someone asked me for my telephone number, and for the first time in my life I . . . give the number without looking in my book. Before I went to Psycho-Clinic I always forgot numbers and names. I . . . remember them at all. Now, thanks to Psycho-Clinic, I . . . remember much more. If I see someone in the street tomorrow, I won't need to hide — I . . . stop and say hello to them.

Eugene, Maryland, USA

I didn't like crowds of people. I . . . go to the theatre or the cinema. I love horse racing, and I . . . go to the races. But the people at Psycho-Clinic . . . stop me feeling afraid. Now I . . . do all those things. Yesterday I . . . stand in a crowd at a baseball game. I . . . lead a normal life now. There's an interesting show at the local theatre next week, and I . . . see it.

be allowed to and have to

Complete this article about learning to drive in Britain. Put in a positive or negative form of *be allowed to* or *have to*.

In Britain you ... drive a car when you're seventeen. You ... get a special two-year driving licence before you can start. When you're learning, someone with a full licence always ... be in the car with you because you ... take the car on the road alone. You ... go to a driving school — a friend can teach you. The person with you ... take money for the lesson unless he's got a teacher's licence.

Before you ... have a full licence, you ... take a driving test. You can take a test in your own car, but it ... be fit for the road. In the test you ... drive round for about half an hour and then answer a few questions. If you don't pass the test, you ... take it again a few weeks later if you want to. In 1970 a woman passed her fortieth test after 212 driving lessons! When you've passed your test, you ... take it again, and you ... go on driving as long as you like, provided you are fit. Britain's oldest driver was a Norfolk man who drove in 1974 at the age of 100.

Before 1904 everyone ... drive, even children. Then from 1904 motorists ... have a licence. But they ... take a test until 1935. In the early days of motoring, before 1878, cars ... go faster than four miles an hour, and someone ... walk in front of the car with a red flag.

Activity

Write a few sentences about learning to drive in your country.

be allowed to and have to

Here are some rules and information for campers at the Riverside Camping Centre.

> You must pay on arrival.
> You musn't light fires.
> You musn't play ball games.
> You must leave before ten o'clock in the morning.
> You needn't worry about food—there's a shop at the Centre.

When Paul and Diane arrived at the camp site, they looked at the rules. What did Paul and Diane say?

Example: We have to pay on arrival.
1 We aren't ...   2 ...   3 ...   4 ...

When they got home, Paul and Diane told their friends Mike and Wendy about the camp site.

Example: We had to pay on arrival.
5 ...   6 ...   7 ...   8 ...

Mike and Wendy decided to stay at the camp site during their next holiday. They talked about it before they went.

Example: We'll have to pay on arrival.
9 ...   10 ...   11 ...   12 ...

Activity

Talk to the other members of the class about rules at schools and colleges in your country. When do students have to be there? Are there some things they aren't allowed to bring into class? etc. If you've left school, say what the rules were when you were there.

must and mustn't

Do you know what these signs mean? Use *You must* … and *You mustn't* … with these words: *turn round, go straight on, overtake, put some money in, smoke, stop, take photos, turn left, turn right, go faster than.*

Examples

You must put
some money in.

You mustn't
turn left.

1

2

3

4

5

6

7

8

9

Activity

Can you think of any other signs that say what you must or mustn't do? Describe a sign to your partner and ask him/her what it means.

must, needn't and mustn't

Helen isn't very well today. She's in bed. She's been sick, and she's quite hot. The doctor has come to see her. Complete what the doctor says. Put in *must, mustn't* or *needn't.*

Doctor Well, I'm going to give you some medicine. You … take it four times a day before meals. And go on taking it even if you feel better. You … stop taking it until you've finished the bottle. You … drink all of it. Now, you … stay in bed today. It's the best place for you at the moment. You can get up tomorrow if you like. You … stay in bed all the time when you start to feel better. But you … go outside this week. It's too cold. And you really … do any work at all. You need absolute rest. You … just relax for a few days. You can eat a little if you like, but you … if you don't want to. But don't forget to keep drinking. You … drink as much water as you can. You'll probably be all right again next week, so you … call me again unless you feel worse. But I'm sure the worst is over.

Activity

Imagine that your partner has a bad cold. What would you recommend him/her to do?

31

ought to and might

The picture is from a booklet about safety in the home. Say what's wrong and what the dangers are. Use *ought to* and *might*.

Example

There oughtn't to be a cloth on the table. The baby might pull it off.

Activity

Imagine that tomorrow you plan to go on a 15-mile walk in the country with three or four other people in your class. Discuss with them what you ought to wear and what you ought to take with you. Give reasons for your suggestions.

Ex There's a cloth on the table. There's a danger that the baby will pull it off.

1 The pills aren't in a safe place. There's a danger that the baby will eat them.

2 There's a hole in the carpet. There's a danger that someone will fall over.

3 The towel is over the cooker. There's a danger that it will catch fire.

4 The drawer isn't shut. There's a danger that it will fall out.

5 There's some broken glass on the floor. There's a danger that someone will step on it.

6 There isn't a plug on the kettle. There's a danger that someone will get an electric shock.

would

Sadie is doing a test to find out what kind of personality she has. She has to answer a lot of questions about what she would do in different situations. Here are some of the questions with Sadie's answers. Say what Sadie *would* and *wouldn't* do.

Example

She would go to the party. She wouldn't go to the cinema.

100 You want to go out one evening. You decide to go to a cinema. Then a friend invites you to a party. Where would you go?

☐ to the cinema ☑ to the party

101 You are walking through a forest on a warm day when you come to a wide river. You can either swim the fifty metres across the river or walk an extra kilometre to the nearest bridge. Which would you do?

☐ swim ☑ walk

102 You find a £10 note in the street. What would you do with it?

☑ keep it ☐ take it to the police

103 You are on a bus. There are two people sitting and talking in front of you. You don't know them. You hear your name mentioned in the conversation. What would you do?

☑ listen ☐ move to another seat

104 You have to choose between two jobs. One is interesting but not well paid. The other is boring but well paid. Which would you choose?

☐ the interesting job ☑ the well paid job

105 You are travelling on a plane to England. The man sitting next to you offers you £5,000 to take a small packet through Customs for him. What would you say?

☐ yes ☑ no

106 You are driving along a country road when you see a car by the side of the road. The driver is standing and waving at you. He wants you to stop. What would you do?

☐ stop ☑ drive on

Activity A

Say what *you* would do in these situations.

Activity B

There's a television programme in Britain called 'Jim'll Fix It'. A man called Jimmy Savile appears on the programme. People write to him and say what they would like to do but have never been able to do. People want to parachute from aeroplanes, sing in a pop group, play tennis at Wimbledon, and so on. Jim fixes it so that they can do these things, and we see their wishes coming true on television. Imagine that it's your turn to do what you like. What would you do?

could, must and can't

Milena and Ahmed are students of English. They're doing this crossword. Milena is reading out the clues, and Ahmed is suggesting possible answers.

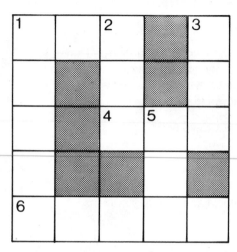

Across

1 You write with it.
4 Past tense of 'be'.
6 It carries things by road.

Down

1 Person learning something.
2 Opposite of 'old'.
3 You pay to ride through the streets in it.
5 Planes travel in it.

Complete their conversations about each clue. Write the sentences with *It could* …, *It can't* … and *It must* …. Here are the words that Ahmed suggests: *bus, taxi, new, young, pen, pencil, sky, air, student, pupil, van, lorry, was, were.*

Example

Milena *One across. You write with it.*
Ahmed *It could be 'pen' or 'pencil'.*
Milena *It can't be 'pencil'. It must be 'pen'.*

1 **Milena** Four across. Past tense of 'be'.
  Ahmed It could be … .
  Milena It can't … . It … .

Go on.

Activity

Do this crossword with a partner. Discuss the possible answers together.

Across

1 Give information.
3 A number.

Down

1 It's bigger than a village.
2 Like very much.

47 (BEG 7.1–7.12)

Modal verbs

Adam, Lisa, Don and Melanie are students. They were on their way to visit some friends last week in Adam's car when it broke down. Complete the conversation by putting in one of the following: *can, can't, could, must, mustn't, needn't, ought to, should, might, 'll, will, won't, shall, would*. (Sometimes more than one answer is correct.)

Lisa What's the matter? Why have you stopped?

Adam There's something wrong. It isn't going properly.

Don Let's have a look.

Lisa We … be out of petrol, I suppose.

Adam We … be out of petrol. We only got some half an hour ago.

Lisa Well, if there is something wrong, … you put it right, do you think?

Adam Give me a chance. I don't know what the trouble is yet.

Melanie Look at this steam. The engine … be too hot.

Don Don't take the cap off the radiator. You … do that. You … get boiling water all over you.

Adam If it's too hot, we … have to wait until it cools down.

Lisa And how long … that take?

Don We … wait about half an hour before we go on.

Melanie I suppose there … be something else wrong with it.

Lisa We passed a garage about a mile back. I suppose they … come and have a look at it if we ask them.

Adam The car … be all right. Our local garage has just serviced it. I paid £30 for a full service.

Don You … worry. I'm sure it's just got too hot. Let's wait a bit.

Lisa We … be late now, I expect.

Melanie There's some coffee in the back of the car. … we have some while we're waiting? There are some sandwiches, too.

Don I'm starving. I … have something to eat.

Melanie … you like a sandwich, Lisa?

Lisa No, thanks. I … eat bread. I'm on a diet.

Adam We … phone Matthew if we're going to be late.

Don We … be very late, I don't think.

Melanie You … buy a new car, Adam.

Adam Well, it … be nice if I had the money. But I'm afraid we … have to put up with this old thing for a little longer.

Activity A

Act out the conversation in groups of four.

Activity B

Work in groups of four again. Imagine that you are about to go on a 300-mile car journey along a motorway. Discuss what to do about food on the journey.

48 (BEG 7.14)

Modal verbs + **be** + -ing form

Emma and Sadie are students. They've both got exams tomorrow. Complete their conversation using a modal verb + *be* + the -ing form of each verb in brackets. Use the modal verbs *ought to, might, must* and *would*.

Example

You (do) some work.
You ought to be doing some work.

Emma Hello, Sadie. Aren't you doing any work? You (revise) for the exams.
Sadie I (read) my notes if I had them, but I've lost them.
Emma Good Lord! How awful! Do you want to look at mine?
Sadie No, thanks. It's okay. Don't worry, Emma. Exams aren't important.
Emma Not important! You (joke)! I (look) everywhere if my notes were lost.
Sadie Well, I'll probably find them before tomorrow.
Emma Have you seen Lisa? She's got a book of mine.
Sadie She was in here not long ago. Perhaps she's outside. She (sit) in the garden.
Emma I'll go and have a look. Then I (go). I have to get to the library before it closes.
Sadie What are you doing tonight, Emma?
Emma Revising, of course. Aren't you?
Sadie I (play) tennis with Rebecca. If the weather stays fine, that is. It'll be too late for revision tonight.

Activity

Say what you would be doing at the moment if today was a different day of the week. Find out what the other members of the class would be doing (or might be doing) if it was a Saturday or a Sunday.

49 (BEG 7.15)

Modal verbs + **have** + -ed form

Last night Lord Milton was found dead in his study at his home in Devon. Someone shot him. Detectives are trying to find out who the murderer is. Read what the detectives are thinking and add a sentence with a modal verb + *have* + -ed form. Use *must, might, couldn't* or *shouldn't*.

Example

Lord Milton was shot in the head from about two feet. He certainly died instantly.
He must have died instantly.

1 His wife Lady Evelyn found the body. She picked the gun up from the carpet. It was a mistake to touch it.
2 The doors and windows were locked. The murderer was certainly one of the five people in the house.
3 Lord Milton had made a new will. He wanted to leave some money to his secretary Warren Digby. It's a pity he told anyone about it.
4 We can't find the will. Perhaps the murderer took it.
5 Lord Milton's daughter Barbara was ill last night. It was impossible for her to walk to the study.
6 The writer Felicity Gray is staying in the house. She's writing the life story of Lord Milton. Why would she kill him? But it's possible.
7 It doesn't make sense for Warren Digby to take the will. It's impossible.
8 Barbara's husband John was in London yesterday. Lady Evelyn says he rang her in the evening from his club. It's certain he was in London.

Activity

Discuss the murder and write three or four more sentences about it using a modal verb + *have* + -ed form.

Modal verbs

Nils and Oskar are spies. They're sitting in a car near the border between Silonia and Omagua. They're waiting for Harry. Put in a modal verb, (positive or negative), *be able to, be allowed to* or *have to*. (Sometimes more than one answer is correct.)

Nils Where's Harry, then? I … see him.
Oskar Yes, we said seventeen hours. He … be here by now.
Nils He might not … find the place. He … have crossed the border in the wrong place.
Oskar Impossible! Harry … have made a mistake. You know Harry.
Nils Well, I hope he comes soon.
Oskar It's the most important job he's ever done for us. He absolutely … get the information.
Nils I've often wondered about Harry. You don't think he … be working for the other side?
Oskar No, I don't. Harry is one of us.
Nils Well, I just think this job has been easy for him so far. Too easy. Perhaps the Omaguans know all about Harry. Someone … have told them about the job. They … have a man in our organization.
Oskar I don't believe it. They're not clever enough. But Harry is clever.
Nils But you … be sure. What if it was true?
Oskar It … be the end for us, of course. But it isn't true.
Nils Harry takes a lot of risks. He does dangerous things. The boss lets him do what he wants. Harry shouldn't … put other people in danger. I told the boss, but he didn't listen. He … have listened to me.
Oskar Shut up, will you? Harry is a good man. Only Harry … do this job.
Nils It's seventeen oh two. We're late.
Oskar You're right. We … go at once. We … stay here any longer.

Nils We've waited and he hasn't come. We … have driven here at all.
Oskar We had to be here. Harry … have come. He … have done if he'd been able to.
Nils Just a minute. There's someone behind that tree. Two men, I think. They … be watching us. Why else … they be here?
Oskar Right. Have your gun ready. We may … shoot our way out.
Nils OK, I'm ready.
Oskar Let's go then. Come on!
Nils The car … start! Oh, my God! Where's my gun? Give me my gun!
Oskar Put your hands up. Get out of the car! Lie down!
Nils It was you, Oskar! You told the Omaguans about Harry, didn't you? You … be mad. Oh, my God!

Activity

Imagine that it is fifteen minutes after the start of your lesson and the teacher still hasn't arrived. Discuss the situation and decide what to do.

51 (BEG 8.1)

Negative statements

People are going to vote for a new government soon. Tony and Jackie are arguing about who to vote for. Complete the conversation, replying to a positive statement with a negative one each time.

Example

Jackie I like Betty Root.
Tony *I don't like her.*

Jackie Betty Root would be a good Prime Minister. People should vote for her.
Tony They … for her, you mean. She'd be no good. George Wright's party is the best.
Jackie It …, you know. Betty Root's party is the best. Her people have got the right ideas.
Tony … at all. Remember what happened when Root was Prime Minister? She made mistakes.
Jackie … . She did well. She took the right decisions.
Tony I'm afraid … .
Jackie Things were OK in Betty Root's time.
Tony … you know. They were terrible.
Jackie Betty understands our problems.
Tony … . But George Wright does. He's been a good Prime Minister.
Jackie … . He's been awful.
Tony George is popular. People like him.
Jackie …, I tell you. They're tired of him.
Tony George Wright will win.
Jackie … . Betty Root will. I'm sure of that.

Activity

Comment on these three statements and say in what way they are wrong.

1 London is the biggest city in the world.
2 A person can live for weeks without food or water.
3 The Americans sent the first satellite into space.

52 (BEG 8.2)

Questions

Earlier this evening a man walked into Dixie's wine store, held a gun to the manager's head and got away with £3,000. The police have a description of the man and of the car he was driving. They think the gunman was someone called Lennie Walsh. A detective is questioning Lennie. Complete the conversation, putting in the questions.

Detective Think back to half past six this evening, Lennie. … ?
Lennie Where was I? I don't know. I was walking somewhere. Yes, I went for a walk.
Detective … for walks?
Lennie No, not often, but I did tonight.
Detective … ?
Lennie No, I didn't go to Dixie's wine bar.
Detective … ?
Lennie Yes, of course I've got a car. It's a Mavis Corona.
Detective … ?
Lennie Blue. Look, … ?
Detective I'm asking you all these questions because there's been a robbery. Now, the number of the car. … ?
Lennie No, I don't know it. I can't remember numbers.
Detective Well, I can help you. I think it's BDX 25S. … ?
Lennie Well, you *may* be right. I'm not sure.
Detective … the car?
Lennie No, I didn't. I never steal.
Detective I'm very interested in your car, Lennie. … ?
Lennie I don't know. I've no idea where it is. Someone's borrowed it.
Detective Well, … ?
Lennie A man I know.
Detective … ?
Lennie No, I can't. I can never remember names.

Detective You forget names too, do you? Well, let's talk about your walk. … ?
Lennie I went to the park.
Detective … ?
Lennie No, no one saw me. Well, I don't *think* anyone saw me.
Detective … ?
Lennie No, I didn't see anyone I know.
Detective …, Lennie?
Lennie What do you mean — am I going to tell you the truth? I'm telling it *now*.
Detective You went out for a walk! No one saw you!
Lennie Well, *someone* saw me. I've just remembered.
Detective … ?
Lennie It was a policeman. He's called Phil Grady. He spoke to me in the park. I know him well — he's arrested me twice.
Detective … this?
Lennie Oh, about half past six, I think.
Detective Just a minute. I'm going to make a phone call.

Activity A

Act out the interview with a partner.

Activity B

Imagine that *you* are the detective. You discover from Phil Grady that Lennie's story is true — Grady spoke to him at half past six. What questions would you now ask Lennie?

53   (BEG 8.2; 8.3)

Positive and negative questions with **why**

Yesterday a Puffco petrol tanker crashed into a house and exploded, killing four people. The Daily Talk is looking into the accident, which happened in the village of Hamleigh. Look at the information that the newspaper has found and ask some questions.

Examples

Why was the fire station at Upstone closed last year?
Why didn't the fire brigade arrive until twenty minutes after the accident?

	There was once a fire station at Upstone, two miles away. *It was closed last year.* The fire brigade were slow. *They didn't arrive until twenty minutes after the accident.*
1	Puffco are trying to save money. *Their tankers aren't serviced until they break down.*
2	The driver was breaking the law. *He had been on the road for nine hours.*
3	The warning sign was knocked down a month ago. *It wasn't put up again.*
4	There's no speed limit, even for lorries. *They're allowed to go as fast as they like.*
5	The villagers have protested. *The police haven't taken any notice of them.*
6	A by-pass was planned thirty years ago. *It hasn't been built.*
7	Puffco told their drivers not to use the route. *They still use it.*
8	There have been accidents in the past. *We haven't learned any lessons from past accidents.*

Activity

What questions might the Daily Talk ask about a fire at a dance hall in which thirty young people died?

54 (BEG 8.5)

Negative question tags

All the pupils who left Parkside School twenty years ago are having a reunion. They're meeting to talk about the old days when they were younger. Put in the missing tags.

Roger Hello. You're Wendy, … ?
Wendy Yes. I remember you, too. You're Roger Cowley.
Roger That's right. We were in the same class, … ? But it's easy to forget people, … ?
Wendy I think I remember most of the people here. Jessica Squires is over there. She reads the news on Television North-West, … ?
Roger Yes, she's on television quite often. She's done well, … ?
Wendy We had a lot of fun at school, … ?
Roger Er, yes. Don't turn round, but Malone's looking this way.
Wendy Mike Malone?
Roger Yes, you can remember him, … ?
Wendy Oh, yes.
Roger I hated him. Oh, no! He's coming over here.
Wendy Well, it is a reunion. We ought to be friendly, … ?
Mike Hello, Roger. Nice to see you again.
Roger Nice to see you too, Mike.
Mike This reunion was a good idea, … ?
Roger Yes, I'm enjoying it. Mike, do you remember Wendy?
Mike Yes. She's my wife.
Roger Oh!

Activity

Imagine that in twenty years' time you are at a reunion with the other members of your class. Think of three or four sentences with question tags that you might say to your partner.

55 (BEG 8.5)

Positive and negative question tags

Peter, Sue and Bob are football fans. They're talking about the World Cup. Complete their conversation by putting in the question tags.

Peter Did you see Holland and Mexico on television last night?
Bob Yes, it was a great game, … ? Holland were marvellous.
Sue They won't find it so easy against Poland, … ?
Bob No, they won't. Poland have got a good team, … ?
Peter Lobak looks good, … ? The Austrians couldn't stop him, … ?
Bob It'll be an interesting game, … ?
Sue England haven't been very good, … ?
Bob Luck hasn't been on our side, … ?
Sue But why is Bodger playing? He isn't very good, … ?
Peter He didn't play very well against Peru, … ?
Bob He doesn't play as well now as he used to, … ?
Peter Well, we should beat Nigeria, … ?
Sue I don't know. Anything could happen, … ?
Bob The West Germans are good, … ? They don't take any risks, … ?
Peter They're playing Hungary tonight. You'll be watching, … ?
Bob Yes, of course.

Activity A

Talk to a partner about a sporting event. Try to use a few positive and negative tags in your conversation.

Activity B

If you aren't interested in sport, talk to your partner about a television programme you both watch or about world events which have been on the radio lately.

Short additions to statements

Look at the notes about three cars in the table below.

First, write eight sentences (1–8) giving information about the cars. Use *but* in those sentences.

Examples

The Prince isn't easy to drive, but the Delta and the Swift are.
The Prince and the Swift feel comfortable, but the Delta doesn't.

1 The Prince and the Delta … . (Go on in this way.)

Then write another eight sentences (9–16). In each sentence mention the two cars which have the same answer. Use *so* or *neither*.

Examples

The Delta is easy to drive, and so is the Swift.
The Prince feels comfortable, and so does the Swift.

9 The Prince …, and neither … . (Go on in this way.)

Activity

Think of some similarities and differences between the capital of your home country and London. Talk about the two cities using *so*, *neither* and *but*.

	Prince	Delta	Swift
Is it easy to drive?	no	yes	yes
Does it feel comfortable?	yes	no	yes
Does it look good?	no	no	yes
Can it do 150 kilometres an hour?	no	no	yes
Does it use less than ten litres of petrol per 100 kilometres?	no	yes	no
Is it cheap to repair?	yes	yes	no
Has it got four doors?	yes	no	yes
Has it got a lot of room inside?	no	yes	yes
Did it win a 'Road' magazine prize last year?	yes	no	no
Is it good value?	yes	no	no

57 (BEG 9.2)

so and **not** after a verb

Paul and Diane are going to Tony's party. Complete their conversation using the verbs in brackets. Do not put a whole clause after the verb. Use *so* or *not* if necessary.

Example

No, (expect).   *No, I don't expect so.*

Diane I hope this party's good.
Paul (hope), too. I don't know how we're going to get there.
Diane Is the car still out of action?
Paul (be afraid).
Diane What's the matter with it?
Paul (be sure), but I think it's something electrical.
Diane Haven't you taken it to the garage yet?
Paul (be afraid). I haven't had time.
Diane Well, Martin will be going, won't he? We can ask him for a lift.
Paul Yes, (suppose). I don't imagine there's a bus.
Diane I (expect). Not in the evening.
Paul OK, I'll ring Martin. He might be taking Richard, of course.
Diane Oh, (hope). That man talks about horse racing the whole time. He's so boring.
Paul Yes, (know).
Diane Do we have to take a bottle to this party?
Paul No, (think). Tony didn't say.
Diane We'd better take some wine. There's a bottle in the cupboard.

Activity

React to these three questions using similar sentences with *hope*, *think* etc.

☐ Is there going to be a Third World War?
☐ Have people from other planets visited the earth?
☐ Is there life after death?

58 (BEG 9.3)

Leaving out words

A British reporter is at the Olympic Games. Look at her notes and combine each pair of sentences into one. Use *and* or *but* and leave some of the words out.

Examples

The Russians are first in the medals table.
The Americans are second in the medals table.
The Russians are first in the medals table and the Americans second.

The British team have won three silver medals.
They haven't won a gold medal.
The British team have won three silver medals but not a gold medal.

1 Polinski won the long jump.
   McCall won the high jump.
2 Ivor Ketapov won't be running in the 100 metres.
   No one knows why he won't be running in it.
3 He holds the 200 metres world record.
   He doesn't hold the 100 metres world record.
4 British runners have broken records.
   British swimmers haven't broken records.
5 A Frenchman is leading in the marathon.
   A Swede is leading in the cycle race.
6 There were big crowds on Tuesday.
   There weren't big crowds on Wednesday.

Activity

Write similar sentences on these topics.
Use two clauses linked with *and* or *but*.

☐ Corsica and Sardinia
☐ John F. Kennedy and Edward M. Kennedy
☐ dinosaurs

Replacing words and leaving out words

Milena and Ahmed are students. They're going to take an English exam soon. Their English is correct, but they could improve it by replacing or leaving out words. Can you help them to make the underlined sentences shorter? Use short additions to statements, use *so* and *not* after a verb, or leave out words instead of saying them again.

Milena It's the English exam in two weeks. Have you done any work for it?
Ahmed No, I'm afraid I haven't done any work for it. I haven't had much time lately.
Milena And I haven't had much time. I've been very busy.
Ahmed I've been to all the classes, though. And I've done the homework.
Milena I haven't done the homework. I always have so many other things to do in the evenings.
Ahmed There's an oral exam, isn't there?
Milena Yes, I think there's an oral exam. Mrs Moss mentioned it last week in one of our lessons.
Ahmed I can do written work all right, but I can't do oral work.
Milena Oh, nonsense. Your spoken English is very good. You can hold conversations in English, can't you?
Ahmed Yes, I suppose I can hold conversations in English. Perhaps I'll do all right. Are we allowed to use dictionaries in the exam, do you know?
Milena I don't think we're allowed to use them. Why don't you ask Mrs Moss?
Ahmed Yes, I will ask her. She'll know, won't she?
Milena I expect she'll know.
Ahmed I really must pass the exam.
Milena Will you need English in your job?
Ahmed I'll need it to get a good job.

Milena I'll need it, too. But don't worry, Ahmed. Your English is fine. You're going to pass.
Ahmed Well, I hope I'm going to pass. I know you will pass.
Milena I wish I could be so sure. I'm certainly not looking forward to it.
Ahmed And I'm not looking forward to it. I'll be glad when it's over, in fact.
Milena I'll be glad, too.

Activity A

When you have improved the conversation, act it out with a partner.

Activity B

Talk to your partner about the English exam you will both take or about whether you will need to use English in your job or as a visitor to an English-speaking country.

The passive: simple present tense

These pictures show what happens when you post a letter. Write a sentence for each picture using the passive voice.

Activity

Describe in a few sentences the process that leads to a tin of Australian peach slices being on the shelf of a British supermarket.

Example

A letter is posted.

Ex posting a letter

1 emptying the post box

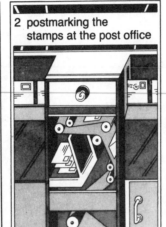

2 postmarking the stamps at the post office

3 sorting the letters into the different towns

4 loading the mail into the train

5 unloading the mail bags after their journey

6 taking the bags to the post office

7 sorting the letters into the different streets

8 delivering the letters

61 (BEG 10.1)

The passive: simple past tense

Complete this short article about the ship 'Mary Rose'. Put the verb into the correct simple past form. Some verbs are active, and some are passive.

The warship Mary Rose (build) in the years 1509–10. In 1544 England (start) a war against France, and in 1545 French ships (send) across the Channel towards England. Some English ships (go) out from Portsmouth to meet them. One of these ships was the Mary Rose. It was carrying 91 guns and 700 men — twice as many as normal. It (sink) quickly to the bottom of the sea even before it (attack) by the French. About 650 men (die). This terrible accident (see) by the king of England himself.

The next month an attempt (make) to raise the Mary Rose, but it (fail). The ship (forget) for hundreds of years.

In the 1970s new plans (make) to raise the ship. Thousands of objects (bring) up from the ship by divers. Then, on 1st October 1982, the Mary Rose (lift) out of the sea. Many people (see) the raising of the ship on television. Finally the Mary Rose (take) into Portsmouth dock 437 years after she had sunk.

Activity

Use these notes to write a paragraph about a ship called the 'Cutty Sark'.

famous sailing ship – built in the 1860s – brought tea from China – later wool from Australia – owned by many different people – finally brought into dry dock in London in 1954 – made into a museum

62 (BEG 10.2)

by + agent

Answer the quiz questions using the passive and by + agent.

Example

Who invented radio?
Bell, Edison or Marconi?
It was invented by Marconi.

1 Who won the World Cup at football in 1982? Brazil, Italy or West Germany?
2 Who wrote stories about a French detective called Maigret?
Agatha Christie, Ellery Queen or Georges Simenon?
3 Who killed Martin Luther King?
John Wilkes Booth, Lee Harvey Oswald or James Earl Ray?
4 Who invented television?
John Logie Baird, Alexander Graham Bell or Thomas Edison?
5 Who built the pyramids?
The Egyptians, the Greeks or the Romans?
6 Who directed the film Gandhi?
Attenborough, Fassbinder or Hitchcock?
7 Who spoke the words 'To be or not to be?'
Alexander, Hamlet or Julius Caesar?
8 Who played James Bond in the first Bond film?
Sean Connery, George Lazenby or Roger Moore?

Activity

Discuss possible answers to these questions.

☐ How are road accidents caused?
☐ Who buys expensive pictures?
☐ How do department stores and industrial companies lose a lot of goods that are never paid for?

63 (BEG 10.3)

The passive: present perfect tense

Write the newspaper headlines as sentences using the present perfect. Some sentences are active and some are passive.

Examples

COST OF LIVING GOES UP
The cost of living has gone up.

GOODS DAMAGED IN FIRE
Some goods have been damaged in a fire.

1 MAN KILLED IN MOTORWAY ACCIDENT
2 OLYMPIC GAMES BEGIN
3 CHILDREN INJURED IN GAS EXPLOSION
4 PICTURE STOLEN FROM MUSEUM
5 CHARLES AND DIANA ARRIVE IN INDIA
6 SECRET PAPERS LOST
7 FAMOUS HOUSE SOLD TO AMERICAN
8 RAY JENKS WINS IMPORTANT RACE
9 DEAD BODY FOUND IN PARK
10 50 'STYLE' SHOPS BOUGHT BY WILSON-MCARTHUR GROUP

Activity

Think of some items of news, or find them in a newspaper. Write five or six sentences about things that have happened recently. Use present perfect active and passive sentences.

64 (BEG 10.4)

The passive: present continuous tense

A dead body has been found, and the police have arrived on the scene. Say what is happening. Use the passive form of the present continuous.

Example

The body is being examined.

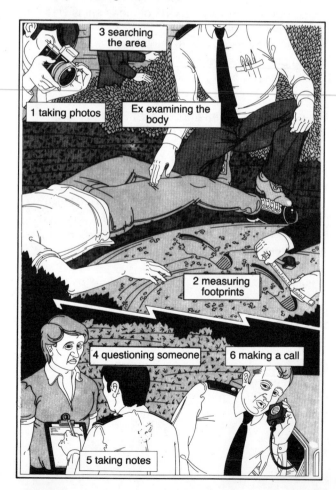

Activity

Talk about these photos and say what is happening.

The passive:
will and other modal verbs

Electrobrit is a company that makes washing machines. At the moment it isn't selling enough machines. The Directors are having a meeting to discuss the problem. Write down their words as they might be reported in a written summary of the meeting. Use the passive.

Example

'We all know we can expect a difficult time, of course.'
A difficult time can be expected.

1 'We have to reduce costs, you know.'
2 'Of course we must keep the factory open.'
3 'We all agree then that we must take action.'
4 'We should warn the staff, of course.'
5 'We ought to make things clear to them.'
6 'Everyone agrees then that the company will employ no more new staff.'
7 'We all know we can't allow the situation to continue.'
8 'We'll hold the next meeting on May 8th, then.'

Activity

Discuss with other members of your class what you think should be done about the problem of heavy traffic in towns. The following points can be included in your discussion.

☐ road-building
☐ public transport
☐ air pollution
☐ the future of oil as a fuel

The passive

Below is a short article about computers. Put the verbs in brackets into the passive voice. Choose the correct tense, or use the modal verb if one is given.

Examples

These machines (control) by computers nowadays.
These machines are controlled by computers nowadays.

Programmes (can/record) on cassette.
Programmes can be recorded on cassette.

Computers then and now

The world's first electronic computer (build) at the University of Pennsylvania in 1946, although computer-like machines (build) in the 19th century. Computers (sell) commercially for the first time in the 1950s, and a lot of progress (make) since then. Computers are now much smaller and more powerful, and they (can/buy) much more cheaply.

Computers (use) in many fields — in business, science, medicine and education, for example. They (can/use) to forecast the weather or to control robots which make cars. The computer's memory is the place where information (keep) and calculations (do).

A computer cannot think for itself — it (must/tell) exactly what to do. A lot of difficult calculations (can/do) very quickly on a computer.

And computers don't make mistakes. Stories (hear) sometimes about computers paying people too much money or sending them bills for things they didn't buy. These mistakes (make) by the programmers — the people who give the computer its instructions. Some years ago, a computer-controlled rocket belonging to the USA went out of control and (have to/destroy). The accident (cause) by a small mistake in one line of the programme. This mistake cost the USA $18 million.

Criminals have found out that 'computer crimes' are often a lot easier than robbing banks. Hundreds of millions of dollars (steal) from American businesses every year by people changing the information in computers.

Large numbers of home computers (sell) recently, especially in the USA and Britain. People know more about computers than they used to, and computers are playing a bigger part in our lives. Progress (make) all the time. Many people believe we can look forward to the day when even our household jobs like cleaning (do) by computer-controlled robots.

Activity

Write a short paragraph about any one of these things. Use the passive in some of your sentences.

☐ the pocket calculator
☐ the video recorder
☐ the aeroplane

67 (BEG 10.6)

The passive:
direct and indirect objects

The sentences below are from an article about the money paid to famous sports people. Rewrite each sentence beginning with the phrase in bold type.

Examples

They paid the racing driver Bobby Kraft **£200,000** when he won the Grand Prix.
£200,000 was paid to the racing driver Bobby Kraft when he won the Grand Prix.

Their club have promised **the AC Milan team** a new house each if they win the European Cup.
The AC Milan team have been promised a new house each if they win the European Cup.

1 They gave **the tennis player Kathy Duprey** £50,000 for winning a competition.
2 A company has paid the skier Anne Stolberg **£40,000** to advertise ski trousers.
3 A TV company gave **the ice hockey team Phoenix Flyers** $20,000 each to play in front of the cameras.
4 His club pays footballer Wayne Simmonds **£250** for every goal he scores.
5 A company offered **the cyclist Luigi Delgado** £25,000 to advertise a soft drink.
6 Henry Lane will pay **the boxer Howard Duke** $3 million for his next fight.
7 They've promised the London Wonders basketball team **a holiday in the West Indies** if they win the league.

Activity

Talk about jobs and money. Which people are paid a lot of money? Which are paid very little? Which people are given extra things in addition to their pay?

68 (BEG 10.8; 20.9)

have something done;
emphatic pronouns

Mark and Jane are going to buy a house. It's quite cheap, but it isn't in very good condition, so they've had a report made on it. In the report there's a list of what they'll have to do to the house. They've ticked the things they can do themselves. Say which jobs they can do and which they'll need to have done by someone else.

Examples

They can clear the gutters themselves.
They'll need to have the roof repaired.

```
Summary of work needed

Clear the gutters. ✓
Repair the roof.
Re-build the garage wall.
Replace the broken glass. ✓
Lay a new floor in the dining-room.
Repair the bedroom ceiling.
Put in a new kitchen window.
Paint the outside of the house. ✓
Decorate all the rooms. ✓
Check the electrical wiring.
```

Activity A

Say which of the jobs in the list you would do yourself and which you would have done by someone.

Activity B

Say what you can have done at these places.

☐ a laundry   ☐ a photographer's studio
☐ a hairdresser's   ☐ a dry cleaner's
☐ a garage   ☐ a dentist's

69 (BEG 11.1)

if-clause type 1

Charlotte works for an advertising company. She's made some notes about different products. Write sentences with *if* + the simple present + *will* to advertise the products.

Examples

wash your hair with Glam – it looks super
If you wash your hair with Glam, it'll look super.

feel better – take Panadex
You'll feel better if you take Panadex.

1 choose a Sunspot holiday – have a great time
2 sleep a lot better – sleep in a Dreamway bed
3 people notice you – wear Rodeo jeans
4 shop at Kwikbuy – save money
5 use Luxidor paint – your house looks beautiful
6 know what's happening – read the Daily Talk
7 wash with Whizz – your clothes cleaner
8 drive a Delta – not want to drive any other car

Activity

Write a few sentences advertising some other products. Use if-clauses. You can choose real products.

70 (BEG 11.1)

if-clause type 2

Amanda is a secretary. She's grumbling about her new job and her boss. Match each sentence in the first box with one in the second. Rewrite the sentences using *if* + the simple past tense + *would/could*.

Examples

If my boss didn't play golf, he wouldn't be out of the office so much.
If he told me where he was, I could contact him.

> My boss plays golf.
> He doesn't tell me where he is.
> 1 The pay isn't good.
> 2 He gives me so much work.
> 3 His writing is so awful.
> 4 He doesn't listen to me.
> 5 The offices are such a long way from here.
> 6 There aren't any cafés nearby.

> I can't afford a nicer flat.
> I can't contact him.
> I can't read it.
> I have to tell him everything twice.
> I have to stay late.
> I have to take sandwiches.
> I spend so much time on the bus.
> He's out of the office so much.

Activity

What kind of things do parents say to their children when they aren't doing very well with their school work and are getting low marks? Think of three or four sentences with *if* and the simple past tense.

if-clauses types 1 and 2

Hilary Lester works for an organization called Food for the Third World. She's talking on television about the situation in Omagua. Put the verbs in brackets into the correct tense, or use *will* or *would* or their short forms.

Interviewer Miss Lester, what is the situation in Omagua?

Hilary Well, it's very bad. Thousands of people have died, and thousands more (die) soon if they (not get) help. The people have very little food or water. And if we (not do) something soon, things (get) much worse. There will simply be nothing left to eat.

Interviewer Is the British government doing anything to help? If they (send) food, that (help) to save lives, wouldn't it? After all, Omagua was once a British colony.

Hilary Yes, indeed. And the country is very poor, of course. But our government refuses to do anything quickly. They say they need time to find out about the problem. But we haven't got any time. It (be) too late if they (not do) something soon.

Interviewer Well, it doesn't look as if Omagua is going to get any help for the moment. So what next? What (happen) if the country (not get) enough food or enough money to buy food?

Hilary Well, if our government (not be) willing to help, we (have to) ask people to send us money. In fact, we're asking them now.

Interviewer How much are you asking people to give?

Hilary We're asking them just to send what they can. Even small amounts will be welcome. We (be) very grateful if people (send) what they can afford. After all, if everyone in the country (give) just 10p, we (have) a lot of money, wouldn't we? I'm sure if people (know) exactly what things were like in Omagua, they (want) to help.

Interviewer And are you hopeful that **people will** send money?

Hilary Oh, yes. If people (hear) about the problem, as they're doing now, then they (help), I'm sure. They always have done before.

Interviewer Is there still time to get food and money to the people who need it, Miss Lester?

Hilary Oh, yes. We'll put the money to good use immediately. If people (post) money to us tomorrow, the food (be) in Omagua by the end of the week.

Interviewer Well, it's certainly a good thing that you're able to help the Omaguans. If your organization (not exist), things (be) much less hopeful. Now, can you tell us the address where people should send money? …

Activity

Graham and Miranda are on holiday in East Africa. They're in a safari park, and their car has run out of petrol. They're three miles from the nearest filling station, which is just outside the park. They've got a petrol can. There are no other cars in sight. It is very hot, and they have no water. There are lions in the safari park, although they can't see any at the moment.

Discuss possible answers to their problem using if-clauses.

if-clause type 3

Below is the story of what happened when four people went on a long walk last week. Read the story and rewrite the underlined parts using if-clauses type 3.

Examples

If it hadn't rained most of the morning, it would have been a pleasant walk.
They wouldn't have decided to go if the forecast had been bad.

Last Saturday Trevor, Alison, Gary and Emma went on a twenty-mile walk over the Norland Hills. Trevor likes walking, and it was his idea. They walked from Oscroft at the eastern end of the hills to Raveley in the west. The day didn't go at all as planned. It rained most of the morning, so it wasn't a very pleasant walk. The weather is often wet in the Norland Hills, in fact. But they decided to go because the forecast wasn't bad. Trevor and Alison wore their anoraks, but Gary and Emma got wet because they didn't have their anoraks. The four friends had other problems too. They forgot to bring a map, and they lost the way. They wanted to stop for lunch in the village of Rydale. They finally got there at two o'clock. They were late because they didn't go the right way. They had planned to eat at the café in Rydale, but they weren't able to eat there because the cafe was closed for the day. It was very annoying. They didn't have any food with them, so they were hungry. But the weather was better by this time, and they decided to go on to Raveley. Five miles further on Alison had an accident. She fell and hurt her leg. So they had to go more slowly after that. They lost even more time. They missed their bus home because they got to Raveley so late. There wasn't any other transport, so they rang their friend Adam. Luckily he was at home, so he was able to come and fetch them in his car. They were glad to get home.

Activity

Here is part of a newspaper report about a motorway accident. Read it and then write three or four sentences about the accident using if-clauses type 3. You can use your own words as well as the words in the report.

30 DIE IN COACH DISASTER

There was a terrible accident on the motorway near Gondolfo last night when a coach overturned and caught fire. Thirty people died, all of them British. There were only four survivors, who managed to get out through a broken window. Luckily the motorway was quiet and no other vehicle was involved in the crash. The coach, owned by Gladway Tours of London, was on its way to Athens. According to the survivors, the driver had been at the wheel of the coach for fourteen hours and had probably fallen asleep. The coach left London two hours late, and the driver was

if-clauses types 1–3

David, Lynn, Angela and Martin live in a town on a busy main road. They're talking about a plan to build a by-pass round the town.

Complete the conversation by putting the verbs in brackets into the correct form. Use *will* or *would* if necessary.

David I think a new road is a good idea. It (keep) the traffic out of the town if they build a by-pass. The traffic in the High Street is terrible. If they'd had any sense, they (build) a by-pass years ago.
Lynn But what about the shopkeepers? If there was a by-pass, then people (not stop) here. And there'll be fewer customers in the shops if there (be) less traffic in the town.
Angela I don't agree. I think more people (want) to shop here if it's quieter and pleasanter.
Martin Tourists (not come) into the town if there's a by-pass.
David If the High Street (be) less busy, it would be a lot easier to cross the road.
Angela There (be) less noise if there were fewer heavy lorries.
David And the traffic doesn't do the buildings any good. Everything shakes when a heavy lorry goes past. Do you remember those old houses in West Street? They had to knock them down because of damage by lorries. If there (be) a new road ten years ago, they (not have to) do that. And cyclists have been knocked off their bikes by lorries. One man was killed. That (not happen) if the lorries hadn't had to use the High Street.
Martin Don't forget that if you (improve) the road system, then the traffic may simply increase. Or you'll just move the problem to another town.
Angela But look at the situation now — dozens of lorries moving very slowly through the town. It (save)

a lot of time if they travelled more quickly along a by-pass.
Martin The by-pass would use up good farmland that we can't afford to lose.
Lynn The route goes right through Gordon Bentley's farm. It (cut) his farm in two if they build it there. He only bought the farm three years ago.
David Well, if that (happen), they'd pay him for the land.
Lynn He told me yesterday he (not buy) the farm in the first place if he (know).
Angela But a by-pass is for the whole town.
Lynn Well, if I (be) Gordon, I (be) angry about it.
David I'm angry now about the traffic in the High Street. If they (not give) us a by-pass, there'll be trouble, I can tell you.

Activity

Complete these sentences in your own words.

Discuss your answers with other members of the class.

If all goes well, …
If I had a million pounds, …
If there was only one day left before the end of the world, …
If I had lived … hundred years ago, …

74 (BEG 11.2)

if + the simple present tense
+ the simple present tense

There are some 'laws of life' hidden in this table. For each sentence on the left, there is one on the right that follows on from it. Find the pairs of sentences and write the laws. Use *if* and the simple present tense.

Example

If something begins well, it often ends badly.

Something begins well.	They're usually short.
You've got a job to do.	You're probably wrong.
You're in an accident.	You usually make it worse.
You want to buy something.	It often ends badly.
You're absolutely sure about something.	It always takes longer than you think.
You type your own letters.	It's the other person's fault.
You try to make a difficult situation better.	They usually don't make it any more.

Activity A

Discuss the 'laws of life' in the table above and say if you think they are true.

Activity B

Complete these simple 'scientific laws' and write two or three more.

If you mix blue and yellow, you get ... .
If air gets warmer, ...
... a piece of glass with a hammer, ...

75 (BEG 12.2)

Reporting in the present tense

Find out what the horoscope opposite says about the people in the list below.

Examples

Helen (18th November)
It says she is having a difficult time, but there will be some surprises for her.

Paul (6th July)
It says he will have money problems, so it isn't the time to plan his holiday.

1 Bob (13th February)
2 Kate (14th September)
3 David (22nd April)
4 Janet (30th November) and Jerry (10th December)
5 Sarah (3rd October)
6 Tom (12th April)
7 Diane (18th March)
8 Jane (29th May)
9 Mr Johnson (8th January)
10 Sue (4th August) and Peter (20th August)

Activity

Find your horoscope in a newspaper or magazine and tell the other people in your class what it says. If possible, find different horoscopes and compare them.

What the stars say – your horoscope

Aries (21st March – 20th April)
You are worrying a lot, but your problems aren't very great.

Taurus (21st April – 21st May)
You will meet someone interesting, and your life may change suddenly.

Gemini (22nd May – 21st June)
Your boss or teacher will not be pleased with you, but it won't be your fault.

Cancer (22nd June – 23rd July)
You will have money problems, so it isn't the time to plan your holiday.

Leo (24th July – 23rd August)
Everything is going well for you, but you must think before you make any decisions.

Virgo (24th August – 23rd September)
You will have problems at work and you should ask your friends for help.

Libra (24th September – 23rd October)
Your life is getting more exciting, but you must control your feelings.

Scorpio (24th October – 22nd November)
You are having a difficult time, but there will be some surprises for you.

Sagittarius (23rd November – 21st December)
You are feeling rather unhappy, but you will hear some interesting news.

Capricorn (22nd December – 20th January)
You should spend more time with your friends because you are working too hard.

Aquarius (21st January – 19th February)
You will have lots of energy, and you may have to travel.

Pisces (20th February – 20th March)
Your life feels empty, but you will find romance.

---

76 (BEG 12.3)

Reporting in the past tense

Stanley Arnold, the multi-millionaire businessman and head of Arnold Motors, has just died. He wasn't a very popular man. Below are some examples of what the press said about him during his lifetime. Write down what they said.

Example

'Arnold is not a very nice person.' – Today Magazine
Today Magazine said that Arnold was not a very nice person.

1 'Arnold Motors has never paid any tax.' – News Extra
2 'Arnold spends the company's money at a Las Vegas casino.' – Newsday Magazine
3 'When he dies, he will probably leave more than $500 million.' – International News
4 'Stanley Arnold never speaks to his children.' – Modern World
5 'He is planning to leave his money to a dogs' home.' – The Daily Free Press
6 'Arnold has friends in the Mafia.' – World Magazine
7 'The police ought to ask Stanley Arnold some questions.' – The Saturday Reporter
8 'No one will be sorry when he's gone' – The Daily Talk

Activity

Complete the sentences by reporting what people might say in these situations.

After winning a million pounds in a competition, Mrs Grout of Birmingham said …
A plane crashed into the sea, and fifty people were killed. There was one survivor. He told reporters afterwards that …
On the day he became Prime Minister, Mr Wright said …

Reporting questions

Tina has left school but she hasn't got a job yet. Yesterday she had an interview for a job at a pet shop. A man and a woman interviewed her. The next day Tina told her friend Sharon what they had asked her. Give Tina's words.

Examples

They asked me how old I was.
They asked me if I'd had a job before.

Activity A

Think of a job and imagine that you were interviewed for it yesterday. Tell the class what questions you were asked. They have to guess the job.

Activity B

Imagine that you can invite anyone in the world to be your dinner guest. Write down three questions you would like to ask your guest. Tell the other members of your class who you would invite and what you would ask him or her.

Reporting statements and questions

Adam does his shopping at Brisco supermarket. Yesterday a woman who works for Brisco stopped him on his way out and asked him some questions. She wrote the answers on the form below. Later Adam told his friend Don about it. Give Adam's words.

Examples

She asked me how often I shopped at Brisco, and I told her I shopped there twice a week.
She asked me if I was happy to shop there, and I told her I was.

Brisco Supermarkets
Customer questionnaire
How often do you shop at Brisco?   *Twice a week.*
Are you happy to shop here?   *Yes.*
Why do you shop here?   *Because it's cheap.*
Can you get everything you want at Brisco?   *Can't get good bread.*
How far away is your home?   *One mile.*
Have you come here by car?   *Yes.*
How much have you just spent?   *About £15.*
Will you come to Brisco again?   *Yes.*

Activity A

Has anyone ever stopped you in the street or knocked on your door to ask you questions? Have you ever had an interview for a job? Has a reporter or a policeman ever asked you questions? Report the interview to the class.

Activity B

Imagine that one student in your class has won a TV quiz contest. The student tells the class how he/she answered the questions, e.g. 'I said it was Sofia.' You say what the student was asked, e.g. 'Oh, so you were asked what the capital of Bulgaria was.'

Practise the game with a group of other students. Take it in turns to think of an answer to a quiz question.

79 (BEG 12.6)

Reporting orders and requests

Every summer there's a ten-mile 'Fun Run' around Milchester for people who want to keep fit. Last year the organizers gave all the runners a list of rules. Sarah did the run last year, and she's telling a friend what the rules were. Look at the rules and give Sarah's words. Use *tell* or *ask*.

Examples

They asked us to arrive at the start between 1.45 and 2.15.
They told us to be there by 2.30 at the latest.

Milchester Fun Run

Rules for runners

Please arrive at the start between 1.45 and 2.15.
You must be there by 2.30 at the latest.
Please do not park in the centre of Milchester.
You must show your ticket.
You must wear your number on your shirt.
Please wear running shoes.
You must not carry any bags or bottles during the run.
You must follow the correct route.
Please run on the left.
Please do not leave litter.

Activity

What does your English teacher like you to do?
Say if he/she tells or asks you to do these things.

☐ work hard
☐ bring a dictionary to the English lesson
☐ write new words down in a vocabulary book
☐ listen to English programmes on the radio

80 (BEG 12.3; 12.5; 12.6)

Reporting statements, questions, orders and requests

The Anglian bus company wants to stop its service between Milchester and Little Wittering village. An Anglian manager, Mr Budge, is at a meeting in the village. Report what is said.

Examples

'The service is losing money.'
Mr Budge explained that the service was losing money.

'Please try to understand our position.'
He asked the villagers to try to understand the company's position.

1 'Lots of people use the buses.'
  Mr Crane said that …
2 'How can we get to town?'
  Mrs Manston asked …
3 'Most people in the village have got a car.'
  Mr Budge replied that …
4 'You must keep quiet and listen, everyone!'
  The chairman told everyone …
5 'What's going to happen to the school bus?'
  Mrs Davis asked …
6 'It will continue to run.'
  Mr Budge answered that …
7 'The village needs a bus service.'
  Mr Rice said that …
8 'Can you start your own service?'
  Mr Budge wondered …
9 'Can everyone please protest to the government?'
  Mr Hepplestone asked everyone …

Activity

Can you remember the last phone call you made?
Tell the other students what was said during the call.

81 (BEG 12.7)

Reporting suggestions, advice etc.

Magundian soldiers have entered Bingozi, a part of Silonia where a lot of Magundians live. The newspapers are reporting what the Magundians and Silonians are saying. Write down the sentences using *have suggested, have advised* etc.

Example

Magundi Would you like us to sign a peace agreement?
The Magundians have offered to sign a peace agreement.

1 **Silonia** We aren't going to give away Bingozi. It's quite out of the question.
2 **Magundi** We will give full rights to Silonians in Bingozi.
3 **Silonia** You had better think again.
4 **Magundi** Why don't we meet for discussions?
5 **Silonia** You can expect trouble, we're warning you.
6 **Magundi** Would you like to come to Magundi to discuss the problem?
7 **Silonia** If you do not leave Bingozi, we will start a war.
8 **Magundi** It's absolutely essential that we look after our people in Bingozi.

Activity

If you bought a second-hand car that broke down next day and needed expensive repairs, you would probably go back and speak to the salesman you bought it from. What should the salesman offer to do? If the salesman was dishonest, what would he do? What would you do if the salesman didn't want to do anything? Have you any suggestions or advice for people buying second-hand cars?

82 (BEG 13.3)

The unreal present and past after **wish**

Edith is talking to a friend about an old man called Arthur who lives near her. Arthur is a rather sad old man. He has a lot of regrets about what happened in the past and about his present life. Read what Edith says about him and then say what Arthur's regrets are.

Examples

Arthur wishes he didn't live in an old caravan.
He wishes he had married.

Edith Arthur lives in an old caravan. He never married, you know. He can't find work. Well, he left school when he was twelve. He never had a real job of course. And his health isn't good. He hasn't got any friends, poor man. People don't like him. The children are afraid of him. He got into trouble with the police, you know. Well, he never even knew his parents. He had a bad start in life.

Activity

Is there anything in your past that you regret?
Is there anything in your present life that you wish was different? Tell the other members of your class.

83 (BEG 13.2; 13.3)

Tenses in sub clauses

A dangerous criminal called Dan Givens escaped from Maxley Prison a week ago. The police still haven't found him. Detectives Prosser and Jeffs are helping with the search. Complete their conversation, putting the verbs in brackets into the correct tense. Use the simple present, simple past or past perfect tense.

Prosser It's time we (find) Givens, isn't it? And we've still no idea where he is. The way things are going, it'll be Christmas before we (catch) him.

Jeffs I wish Maxley Prison (look) after him a bit better last week.

Prosser If they (discover) the escape more quickly, we'd have had a better chance of getting him.

Jeffs And now we haven't got enough men. If we (have) more men, we'd probably find him.

Prosser We don't even know where his girl-friend is.

Jeffs If only we (know) where she lives now. I bet he's with her.

Prosser We'll get him in the end.

Jeffs I wish they (not let) him escape in the first place.

Prosser When we finally (find) him, he'll probably have a gun.

Jeffs Of course. So we'll just have to be careful. He won't have a chance if he (try) to shoot his way out.

Activity

A tiger has escaped from a zoo and is being hunted by soldiers. What do you think the soldiers might say? Write three or four sentences with *it's time*, *if only*, *when* etc.

84 (BEG 14.2; 14.3)

The infinitive after adjectives and after nouns

Charlotte works for an advertising company. She's made some notes about a number of products. Write two sentences to advertise each product. The first sentence has an infinitive after a noun, and the second has an infinitive after an adjective.

Example

washing some clothes? best with Brite
Have you got some clothes to wash? It's best to wash them with Brite.

1 mowing a lawn? easier with a Swish machine
2 cleaning your shoes? best with Gleem polish
3 doing a dirty job? sensible in Atkinson's work clothes
4 taking some luggage? easier in a car like an Alton Sahara
5 feeding a dog? better Chomp
6 doing a sum? quicker with a Numerex calculator

Activity

Think of some inventions that make work easier or quicker to do. Write a few sentences like *If you've got a carpet to clean, it's easier to use a vacuum cleaner.*

The infinitive after verb + object

Granby United is a very successful football club. It's got a good club chairman and the team manager, Bill Grace, is one of the best in the country. Tim Bennett of the Daily Talk is interviewing people at the club. He's going to write an article about United. Write out Tim's notes as full sentences using verb + object + infinitive. Put *to* with the infinitive if necessary.

Examples

the players don't miss a training period – Bill doesn't allow it
Bill doesn't allow the players to miss a training period.

they train five days a week – he makes them
He makes them train five days a week.

1 they work very hard – Bill makes them
2 they take the game seriously – he forces them
3 the players feel proud of the club – Bill wants that
4 they play well together – Bill teaches them
5 they watch films of other teams – he makes them
6 they can relax after a game – Bill lets them
7 the players have to behave – the club expects it
8 they don't go to night-clubs – Bill doesn't allow it
9 the team does well – the fans want that
10 the club can't win everything – but that's what the fans would like!
11 schoolboys visit the club – Bill invites them
12 local companies are giving money to the club – the chairman has persuaded them

Activity

Discuss the function of a teacher in a class of students. What do you expect a teacher to do? How does a teacher want students to behave? What should a teacher make students do or allow them to do?

86 (BEG 14.9)

The infinitive after the passive

Six members of an organization called Food for the Third World are in Omagua. The group were kidnapped by guerrillas a month ago but have just been released. The leader of the group, Miss Hilary Lester, is telling reporters what happened. Write the sentences as they appear in the newspapers. Use the passive and an infinitive. Remember not to use *let* in the passive.

Examples

'The guerrillas asked me to give them some publicity.'
Miss Lester was asked to give the guerrillas some publicity.

'They made us discuss politics.'
The group were made to discuss politics.

1 'The guerrillas forced us to go with them.'
2 'They made us walk fifty miles to the guerrilla camp.'
3 'The guerrillas didn't let me send a message to anyone.'
4 'They made me carry a heavy bag.'
5 'They expected us to look after injured guerrillas.'
6 'The guerrillas allowed us to move around the camp.'
7 'They let us talk to each other.'
8 'The guerrillas warned me not to try to escape.'

Activity

Up to the year 1865, slavery was allowed in the USA. Write a few sentences saying what a slave's life was like. Use the passive and an infinitive.

87 (BEG 14.10)

for + noun phrase + infinitive

Kelly is a seven-year-old girl whose parents have been killed in a road accident. She's living in a children's home, but she isn't happy there. Two social workers, Valerie and Roy, are talking about Kelly. Rewrite the underlined parts using *for* + noun phrase + infinitive.

Examples

It'll be the best thing for her to live in a family.
It's been very hard for her to accept the situation.

Valerie We've found a family who will have Kelly.
Roy That's excellent. It'll be the best thing if she lives in a family.
Valerie She hasn't accepted the situation. It's been very hard for her.
Roy She hasn't felt at home here. It's been impossible, I'm afraid. Will it take long before the boss gives us a definite decision?
Valerie Well, I've arranged that the psychologist is going to see Kelly on Friday. Then we'll have to wait until she writes her report.
Roy But we're sure, aren't we? There isn't any reason why we should keep her here any longer.
Valerie Oh, it won't be long. It's quite usual that children are in here for months, you know. It would be a mistake if everything happened in a big hurry.
Roy Well, I hope we can explain to Kelly. I think it's important that the children here know about our plans for them.

Activity

Use *for* + noun phrase + infinitive to talk about parties. Do you enjoy parties? Do people have parties in your country? Say what they're like. (*It's usual* …) What makes a good party? (*It's best* … / *It's important* …) What makes a bad one? (*It's a mistake* …).

The infinitive after question words

In 1983 two people from the distant planet Chupron visited the earth. Their names were Kepal and Enis. They looked much like humans. They learnt English before they set off. They travelled in a small spaceship made to look like a Cadillac. They toured the USA pretending to be Canadian tourists. They spoke English the whole time. One day they left the spaceship in West 57th Street, New York while they went for a walk in Central Park. When they came back, it had gone. Look at their conversation and describe their thoughts.

Example

Kepal What shall we do?
Enis I've no idea.
They had no idea what to do.

1 **Enis** How can we get the spaceship back?
  Kepal I don't know.
2 **Kepal** Where should we look?
  Enis I can't think.
3 **Enis** Shall we wait in the street?
  Kepal I'm not sure.
4 **Enis** Where shall we go?
  Kepal I've no idea.
5 **Kepal** Do you think we ought to hide?
  Enis I don't know.
6 **Enis** How can we contact Chupron?
  Kepal I've no idea.
7 **Kepal** Should we go to the police?
  Enis I'm not sure.
8 **Kepal** What do you think?
  Enis I don't know.

Activity

Make similar sentences about these people:

☐ a man who had just finished a meal in a restaurant and discovered that he had forgotten his money
☐ a woman who saw a man on the other side of the street suddenly burst into flames as he was walking along
☐ a man who arrived home from work and unexpectedly found a huge pile of new bricks in his garden completely blocking the way to the door of the house

The infinitive with **to** and without **to**

David has just met an old friend of his called Nigel. They're having a cup of coffee together. Nigel has some bad news. Complete the conversation by putting in an infinitive with *to* or without *to*.
Use these verbs: *answer, borrow, catch, do, find, go, hear, know, lend, look, make, pay, see, spend, stay, think*. (You will need to use some of the verbs more than once.)

David Are you still working for Electrobrit, Nigel?
Nigel No, I'm not. I'm afraid I lost my job there. And Polly's lost her job too. We're having rather a difficult time at the moment.
David Oh, dear. I'm sorry … that.
Nigel I've been out of work for six months now. I expected … a new job fairly quickly, but it isn't so easy, I've discovered.
David Jobs are hard … these days.
Nigel With Polly not working we've very little money … . After I lost my job I managed … my bank manager … us some money, but he won't let us … any more now. And there are lots of bills … . I really don't know what … .
David Do you think you might … a job if you moved somewhere else?
Nigel Well, perhaps. We've talked about it of course. We've even wondered whether … abroad. We could always … a fresh start in a different country. Polly wants me … for a job in America. And I've written to Australia House, although I'm still waiting for them … .
David Do you like the idea of living abroad?
Nigel I don't know really. I think on the whole I'd rather … here if I had a job. But the situation has made us … carefully about our future. We decided we ought … out what opportunities there are. I've agreed … about all the possibilities.
David Well, I hope you find something soon.

Nigel I simply must … a job soon, or I don't know what we shall … .
David Well, let me … what happens, won't you? Look, here's my new address and phone number. Give me a ring some time.
Nigel OK, David. I'd better … now. I've got a bus … .
David I hope … you again soon.
Nigel 'Bye, David.

Activity

Complete these sentences in your own words.

I hope to …
It would be nice to … .
I don't know wh… to …
Why won't they let us … ?
Men/Women are always expected to …

90 (BEG 14.13)

Other forms of the infinitive

Complete this newspaper report in the Daily Talk about the racing driver Chuck Loder. Put the verbs in brackets into an infinitive form. Use the continuous infinitive (e.g. *to be doing*), the perfect infinitive (e.g. *to have done*) or the passive infinitive (e.g. *to be done*).

LODER OUT OF HOSPITAL SOON

Racing driver Chuck Loder, who had a bad accident in last year's Grand Prix, is likely (come) out of hospital soon. He agreed (interview) by our sports reporter, although he has refused (photograph), as his face still shows the marks of the accident.

Chuck was very cheerful when he spoke to us. His health now seems (improve) slowly. He expects (sit) at the wheel once again before very long.

Many people think that last year's race at Bruckheim ought never (take) place. It was the last race on the old track, which is going (re-build) soon. The owners of the track expect (complete) the work in time for next season.

Chuck hopes (drive) in next year's Grand Prix. We wish him luck. Read his personal story of the Bruckheim accident in next week's Daily Talk.

Activity

Write a similar story about a yachtsman called Brendan Stiles who was badly injured when his experimental new yacht overturned and sank during an international yacht race which is held every year off the west coast of Australia.

91 (BEG 15.1)

The -ing form

Look at the objects and say what sports or activities they are used in. Use these verbs: *camp, climb, fish, ride, sail, skate, ski.*

Example

1 *boxing*

Activity

Talk about the different sports and activities with a partner. Say if you like them.

Example

I like swimming. What about you? ~
Well, swimming's OK, I suppose.

Use sentences like these: *I like swimming. Swimming's OK. I don't mind swimming. I don't like swimming much. I hate swimming. Swimming is something I don't do very often.*

92 (BEG 15.2)

The -ing form after conjunctions and prepositions

This is an article about a woman who is head of a supermarket group. Rewrite the sentences with underlining. Use an -ing form after a conjunction or preposition instead of the underlined parts.

Example

After leaving school at 18, Elaine studied business management at Granby Polytechnic.

Elaine Archer is a 34-year-old woman in a very important job. She's head of the huge Brisco Supermarkets group.

Elaine left school at 18 and then studied business management at Granby Polytechnic. She left the Polytechnic, but she didn't take any exams. Elaine decided to see the world and then to make her home in Britain. She spent four years in the USA. She thought about her career during the time she was filling shelves in a supermarket.

As soon as she returned to Britain, Ms Archer bought a small food store. She was soon the owner of a dozen stores in south-east England. She made her stores a success because she pleased the customers. When Brisco took over Archer Stores, Elaine became south-east area manager of Brisco. She has risen to be head of the company in spite of the fact that she is a woman in a man's world. We certainly have not heard the last of her.

Activity

Find out some details of the life of a famous person. Write three or four sentences about the person, using the -ing form.

93 (BEG 15.3; 15.4)

The -ing form after **do** and other verbs

Wendy and Diane are talking about how much help they get from their husbands with the housework. Complete the conversation by putting the verbs in brackets into the -ing form. Put *the* in front of the -ing form where necessary.

Wendy Mike's not much good around the house. Do you get any help from Paul?
Diane Yes, he doesn't mind (help) usually.
Wendy Mike sometimes does (shop), but that's all, really. I have to do all (clean) of course.
Diane Paul does (iron) quite often — that's a great help, because I hate (iron). And he's a very good cook. He usually does (cook) at weekends. We both enjoy (cook), in fact.
Wendy I like (cook) too, but Mike's no good at it. I do (cook) in our house. And I do all (wash). Mike doesn't even know how to use the washing-machine!

Activity

Talk to a partner. Say what jobs you do (or don't do) around the house. Say if you like doing them.

The -ing form after a verb or after a verb/adjective + preposition

Look at what these people are saying and complete the sentences using an -ing form. Put a preposition before the -ing form if necessary.

Example

They're worried about losing their jobs.

Activity

Complete the following sentences in your own words using an -ing form.

I enjoy … I'm afraid …
I believe … I get bored …

They're worried …

1 They insist …

2 He thinks it's wrong to risk …

3 They're tired …

4 She doesn't agree …

5 He wants the government to stop …

6 They believe …

7 She's keen …

8 He doesn't …

95 (BEG 14.5; 15.6)

A noun phrase before an infinitive or -ing form

Amanda is a secretary. She's got a new job, but she doesn't like her boss. She's telling her friend about him. Rewrite each sentence or pair of sentences using an infinitive or -ing form.

Examples

The boss insists on everyone being in the office at nine o'clock.
He doesn't allow us to make personal phone calls.

Amanda Everyone has to be in the office at nine o'clock. The boss insists on it. And we can't make personal phone calls because he doesn't allow it. We don't have coffee breaks because he's stopped that. We have to work hard — that's what he's always telling us. People can't work at their own speed; he doesn't agree with that. I have to work late because he quite often wants me to. If he asked me occasionally, I wouldn't mind. But I have to spend my life at the office. He seems to expect it. And he watches me all the time, which I don't like. People can't be friendly with him — he hates that.

Activity

Write three or four similar sentences about your boss or about your parents. Say what they expect (or don't expect) you to do, or what they insist (or don't insist) on you doing, and so on.

96 (BEG 15.3; 15.7)

The active and passive -ing form

Max Finkel is a famous film director. Max is giving some advice to a friend of his who is going to make a film starring Melinda Burns. Complete what Max says about Melinda using *like, enjoy, love* or *hate* and an active or passive -ing form.

Examples

You might find she makes trouble.
Melinda enjoys making trouble.

Don't ever tell her she's wrong.
She doesn't like being told she's wrong.

1 Let her talk to the press. She …
2 You'd better let them photograph her. Melinda …
3 Don't laugh at her. She …
4 Try to arrange things so that she doesn't have to wait around. Melinda …
5 You'll have to look after her. She …
6 She won't get up early. Melinda …
7 It doesn't matter if people stare at her. She …
8 Never ignore her. She …

Activity

Here is a list of things that many people are afraid of. Are you afraid of them too?

☐ drowning
☐ being bitten by a dog
☐ being stuck in a lift
☐ speaking to a large group of people
☐ being killed in a plane crash

Use *I'm (not) afraid of …*, *I'm terrified of …* or *I (never) worry about …* . Add more things to the list if you can.

The infinitive and the -ing form after verbs

Complete the newspaper article by putting in the infinitive or the -ing form of the verbs in brackets.

NELLIE WILL STAY

Milchester Council has decided (let) 82-year-old Mrs Nellie Battle go on (live) at her home at 29 Croft Street. The Council had wanted (knock) down all the old houses in the street because they were planning (build) a new car park there. The future of this plan is now uncertain.

The story began five years ago when the people of Croft Street agreed (move) to new homes. Unfortunately the Council forgot (ask) Mrs Battle. When they finally remembered her, everyone else had already gone. But the Council failed (persuade) Nellie to do the same. 'My grandson's just finished (decorate) the sitting-room for me,' she said at the time. 'I can't imagine (leave) now.'

The Council offered (pay) Mrs Battle £500 and promised (give) her a new house, but she still refused (move). 'I can't help (like) it here,' she told our reporter. 'I miss (see) the neighbours of course. I enjoyed (talk) to them.' Croft Street has stood almost empty for the last five years. There seemed (be) no way anyone could move Nellie from number 29.

Now comes the Council's new decision. Mrs Battle is very pleased. 'I kept (tell) them I wouldn't move,' she said today. 'I don't mind (be) on my own any more. And I expect (live) till I'm a hundred. I hope (be) here a long time yet.'

We have also heard this week that the Council cannot now afford (build) the car park. One or two of the people who used (live) in Croft Street have suggested (repair) the old houses so that they can move back into them. They dislike (live) in the new houses they moved into five years ago.

Activity

Read this paragraph about the Electrobrit company

The union and management at Electrobrit can't agree. The union wants a five per cent increase in wages. The management say the company hasn't got enough money. If they paid higher wages, they might go bankrupt. But they can give the workers an extra week's holiday next year. The union thinks the wages are very low, and the workers may go on strike.

Think of some sentences that might be spoken during the discussion. Write two or three of the union's sentences and two or three of the management's. Use an infinitive or an -ing form after e.g. *Why do you refuse ..., We can't go on ..., We're offering ..., We can't risk ..., We've promised ...*.

The infinitive without **to** and the -ing form after **see** and **hear**

Mr Pratt often has strange dreams. The pictures on the right show what he dreamed about last night. Describe each dream using *see* or *hear* and either the infinitive without *to* or the -ing form.

Examples

He heard a bomb explode.
He saw a girl running along a beach.

Use these verbs: *burn, crash, fly, jump, ring, scream.*

1 He …. It went on for a long time.
2 … into the sea.
3 … in the sky.
4 …. He thought she would never stop.
5 … out of a car as it was moving.
6 …

Activity A

Write two or three sentences saying what you can see and hear when you look out of your window in the morning.

Activity B

One student imagines that he/she was in a certain place yesterday evening, e.g. at a restaurant or at the circus. The student gives clues, e.g. *I could hear people talking quietly. I saw an acrobat do a somersault.* You guess where he/she was.

99 (BEG 16.2)

The infinitive and the -ing form: special cases

Peter and Sue are in the shopping centre. Complete their conversation by putting the verbs in brackets into the infinitive or the -ing form.

Peter Have we done all the shopping now?
Sue Yes, I think so. I must remember (post) this letter.
Peter I remember (pass) a postbox somewhere.
Sue Just a minute, where's my purse? It isn't in my handbag.
Peter Did you forget (bring) it?
Sue No, I had it not long ago. And my credit card is in there. Oh, my God, what are we going to do?
Peter Just stop (worry) and think. You must have put it down somewhere and forgotten (pick) it up. Try (remember) when you had it last.
Sue I remember (have) it in the shoe shop.
Peter Then you stopped (buy) a newspaper …
Sue Oh, it's all right. It's here in the shopping bag. Sorry. I can't remember (put) it there.
Peter You could try (chain) it to your hand next time.

Activity A

Can you remember things you did when you were very young? Give examples of things you remember doing.

Activity B

Do you ever forget to do things such as turning off lights or locking doors? Give examples.

Activity C

What advice would you give to someone who wants to stop smoking? Use the verb *try*.

100 (BEG 17.1)

The -ing form and the -ed form used as adjectives

Complete the newspaper story about an earthquake in a city called Kitamo. Put in either an -ing form or an -ed form. Use these verbs: *break, burn, cry, damage, fall, frighten, injure, smoke*. (You have to use one of the verbs twice.)

KITAMO EARTHQUAKE

There was an earthquake in the Kitamo region at ten o'clock yesterday morning. It lasted about a minute. Many buildings collapsed. … people ran into the streets. Many were injured by … bricks and stones. After the earthquake, buildings in many parts of the city caught fire. The heat was so great that firemen could not get near many of the … buildings. Hundreds of people have died. The hospital is still standing, but there aren't enough beds for all the … people. Things look very bad in Kitamo now. There are hundreds of badly … houses, and those that caught fire are now just … ruins. The streets are covered with … glass, and … trees block the way. Everywhere there is the sound of … children.

Activity

Imagine that instead of suffering an earthquake, Kitamo and the villages around it were flooded when snow on the mountains suddenly melted, and the River Nor burst its banks after heavy rain. Write a short report on the floods. Try to use -ing forms and -ed forms as adjectives. You can use the verbs in the exercise as well as some of these verbs: *abandon, continue, expect, float, flood, melt, rise, ruin, shiver, worry*.

The -ing form and perfect -ing form in clauses of time

In this story, a British government agent is following a man who he thinks is a spy. Rewrite the sentences under the pictures using an -ing form or a perfect -ing form.

Examples

He left the office carrying a briefcase.
Crossing the road, he bought a newspaper.
Having looked at an inside page, he started walking along Oxford Street.

When he left the office, he was carrying a briefcase.

He crossed the road and bought a newspaper.

After he had looked at an inside page, he started walking along Oxford Street.

1 As he was hurrying along the street, he suddenly stopped outside a travel agency.

2 As he was standing outside, he looked twice at his watch.

3 After he had waited five minutes, he continued along Oxford Street to Hyde Park.

4 He ate a sandwich. He was sitting on a seat.

5 After he had looked again at the paper, he put it in a litter bin.

6 He left the park and stood at the side of the road.

7 He ran into the road and stopped a taxi.

Activity A
Using the pictures on the right, write two more sentences saying what the man did next.

Activity B
Write about a journey you have made recently or about a walk in the country. Include sentences like *Walking through the wood, we saw a fox* or *Having filled up with petrol, we set off*.

In Victoria Street …   Half an hour later …

102 (BEG 17.4)

The -ing form and the -ed form in clauses of reason

A reporter has made some notes about a fire on a passenger aircraft. Combine each pair of sentences. Use the -ed form, -ing form or perfect -ing form.

Examples

The plane was delayed by technical problems. It took off one hour late.
Delayed by technical problems, the plane took off one hour late.

The passengers saw smoke. They became alarmed.
Seeing smoke, the passengers became alarmed.

The pilot had travelled only a short distance from Heathrow. He decided to turn back.
Having travelled only a short distance from Heathrow, the pilot decided to turn back.

1 The airport fire service was warned by air traffic control. It prepared to fight a fire.
2 The passengers believed the aircraft was going to crash. Some of them shouted in panic.
3 The pilot brought the plane down safely. Then he felt very relieved.
4 Everyone was worried by the risk of fire. They hurried to get out.
5 The firemen used chemicals. They soon put out the fire.
6 Most of the passengers had had enough excitement for one day. They put off their journey.

Activity

Write a paragraph telling the story of a group of people who were picked up from the sea by lifeboat men after the boat on which they were passengers had sunk. Some of these words and phrases may be useful: *passenger, alarmed, captain, radio message, life jacket, lifeboat, shocked, experience, hospital.*

103 (BEG 18.1; 18.2)

Plurals of nouns

Complete these paragraphs from a geography book. Put the words in brackets into the plural.

This small country is mostly farmland. The (animal) seen most often are (cow) and (sheep). Most (farm) have a few (goose), too. There are (donkey), but not many (horse). There's a lot of wheat and (potato), and there are (tomato) on the south side of the hills. In summer the (man), (woman) and (child) work together in the (field) seven (day) a week. The (person) work hard all their (life).

The only two (factory) in the country are in the capital. One makes (toy) and (game), and the other makes (knife) and (fork). All these (thing) are for export.

The east of the country is thick forest, the home of wild (pony), (deer) and (wolf).

(Photo) of the (cliff) along the coast show how beautiful the country is. But not many (tourist) visit it because the airport is too small for most (aircraft).

Activity

One student says e.g. *One apple.* The next says *One apple and two books.* The next says *One apple, two books and three cats*, and so on. Each student adds a plural noun beginning with the next letter of the alphabet. If you like, you can use only one type of noun, e.g. the names of animals or things in the house. You can also give points for irregular plurals said correctly.

104 (BEG 18.3)

Direct and indirect objects

At Christmas time in Britain, people usually give presents to their family and to their close friends. It's three weeks before Christmas now. Here is Mrs Bailey's list of presents. There is a tick (√) by those she has already bought. Say what she has bought or is going to give people at Christmas.

Examples

She's bought Kelly an umbrella.
She's going to give Joanne a cassette.
She's bought some chocolates for Jamie.
She's going to give some notepaper to Sadie.

Kelly – umbrella ✓
Joanne – cassette
chocolates – Jamie ✓
notepaper – Sadie
Alan – football
Shaun – watch ✓
camera – Emma
Nick – book ✓
hankies – Angela ✓
Matthew – game
perfume – Gillian ✓
scarf – Laura

Activity

Say if people in your country give presents at Christmas or if they give them at other times of the year. Tell the other students about presents you have given or received recently or that you intend to give.

105 (BEG 18.4; 18.7)

The possessive form and **of**

Give the titles of these pictures in an art gallery. Use the possessive form or *of*.

Examples

chair/dentist
The dentist's chair

club/boys
The boys' club

end/game
The end of the game

1 dog/farmer

2 roofs/houses

3 room/directors

4 supper/children

5 edge/lake

6 rest/walker   7 side/hill

Activity A

Find similar titles for these pictures.

Activity B

In a department store you often see signs like WOMEN'S SHOES or CHILDREN'S BOOKS. Think of some other things that are just for men, women, children, girls or boys.

Countable and uncountable nouns

Mr and Mrs Johnson are going to do some shopping. Mrs Johnson is telling her husband what they need, and he is writing a list. Look at the list and give Mrs Johnson's words.

Examples

'a steak pie'
'some flour'
'a pound of tomatoes'

steak pie
flour
1 lb tomatoes
2 jars marmalade
eggs
pineapple
5 lbs potatoes
sugar
pkt cornflakes
loaf
bananas
3 tins beans
washing powder

Activity

One student says e.g. *Yesterday I went shopping and I bought some coffee.* The next student says e.g. *Yesterday I went shopping and I bought some coffee and a tin of soup.* Each student adds one item to the list. You can either memorize the list or you can take notes, but you must write your list like Mrs Johnson's without using *a, some* or *of*.

107 (BEG 18.11–18.15)

Countable and uncountable nouns; singular and plural forms

Complete this newspaper article. Choose the correct singular or plural forms in the brackets. Begin like this:
The Clayton Clothing Company is going to build a new factory in Milchester. This news …

CLAYTON FACTORY FOR MILCHESTER

The Clayton Clothing Company is going to build a new factory in Milchester. (This/These) (new/s) (was/were) announced by company chairman Mr David Clayton yesterday. Mr Clayton spent the morning in Milchester before returning to the Clayton (headquarter/s) at Granby.

The Clayton company (has/have) been in existence for 130 years and (is/are) famous for its 'Polymode' (good/s). The slogans 'You're never alone with a pair of Polymode (trouser/s)' and 'Polymode (jean/s) (is/are) the (one/s) for you' are well known. The company's profit last year of £2 million (was/were) the highest in the clothing business.

Mr Clayton will not say how (much/many) new (job/s) there will be, but my (information/s) (is/are) that there will be about 500. The (new/s) (is/are) very welcome because (work/s) (is/are) hard to find at the moment, and 2,000 unemployed people (is/are) a high figure for a small town.

Activity A

Make a list of all the clothes you own, e.g. *four coats, about five pairs of trousers, …*

Activity B

Write sentences saying what you think of these things: maths, physics, athletics, economics, politics.

Example: Maths is quite interesting.

108 (BEG 19.1)

a and an

Can you say who these famous people were? Write sentences from the table.

Example

Amundsen was a Norwegian explorer.

Amundsen Cleopatra Confucius Nehru Newton Raphael		a	American Chinese Egyptian English German Indian	composer. explorer. industrialist. painter. philosopher. politician.
Rockefeller Tolstoy Wagner	was	an	Italian Norwegian Russian	queen. scientist. writer.

Activity

Ask the other students some quiz questions that they can answer using similar sentences. You can ask about living people, e.g. *Who is Rudolf Nureyev? Who is Jane Fonda?*

a/an, the and some

Complete the instructions below on how to do an experiment. Decide if each word or phrase in brackets should have *a/an*, *the* or *some* in front of it, or if it should have none of these words.

Experiment

Push (metal rod) through (cork) and then put two pins into (cork), as in Picture 1. Take two more corks and push (nails) into them. Put (pins) on two glasses and move (cork) to (right place) so that it balances, as in Picture 2. Then you need (candle) and (matches). Stand (candle) on (saucer) under one side of (rod) and light it. (Heat) that comes from (candle) will make (metal) expand (= grow bigger). This extra length will make (rod) fall, as in Picture 3. (Experiment) shows that (heat) makes (metal) expand.

Activity

Write about this experiment, which shows that air has weight. Here are some words you can use: *thin, wood, table, stick out, edge, paper, hammer, hit, break, air, press down, weight.*

Nouns with and without **the**

Complete this article about an (imaginary) explorer. Look at each noun or noun phrase in brackets and decide if it should have *the* in front of it.

Thomas French was one of the greatest explorers in (history). He travelled to (South America), (Greenland) and many other parts of (world). He was born in (1886), on (Christmas Day). His family lived near (Regent's Park). They were rich, and (money) was never a problem. Thomas left (school) because he wanted to go to (sea). He sailed across (Atlantic Ocean) with some friends. At twenty he joined an expedition to (Africa). Later he led expeditions to (Andes), to both Poles and even to parts of (USSR). He also climbed (Mount Everest) twice. (History) of all these journeys is in his diaries, which show us (life) of an explorer in the 1920's. (Breakfast) was French's favourite meal, and he always ate well. He went to (bed) early but often got up in (night) to write his diary. He also took hundreds of photos, which are now on show at (National Gallery).

Activity A

Try to find out proverbs or sayings starting with these words:
Time… *Silence*… *Life*… *Practice*… *Honesty*…

Activity B

Describe briefly the journeys you make every day between home and school or work. Say what time you leave and arrive.

Activity C

Make a list of all the places and sights you can think of in London. Tell the other students which sights you have seen or would like to see.

The articles: **a/an** and **the**

Complete the following by putting in *a*, *an* or *the* where necessary. In some places you don't need an article at all.

Graham Mackay is … engineer. He works on … oil rig in … North Sea. He works on … rig for two weeks and then has two weeks at … home in Glasgow. … rig is 100 miles off … coast of Scotland. … oil company's helicopter flies him to and from … Aberdeen Airport. He does … important job, and he's paid over £350 … week.

Graham works twelve hours … day during his two weeks on … rig. His shift finishes at … midnight, when he goes to … bed. Although … work is important, it's rather … boring job. He shares … cabin with three other men. One of them is … friend of his, … American called Lee Driver, who comes from … New Mexico.

… men aren't allowed to drink … alcohol, so Graham has … milk or … tea with his meals. Most of the men smoke … cigarettes.

… weather can be pretty bad. Sometimes there are … storms. Everyone's always glad to get back to … mainland.

Activity

Ask a partner questions and find out the following information. Write down the information.

- ☐ where he/she lives
- ☐ his/her job, or whether he/she is a pupil at school, or a college or university student
- ☐ how many hours he/she works every day
- ☐ what he/she thinks of the job or school

Third person pronouns; **one** and **some**

Some students are thinking of giving a party.
Complete the conversation by putting in *he, him, she, her, it, they, them, one* or *some*.

Don Trevor says we're giving a party on Saturday.
Lisa We're thinking of giving …. … was Alison who first thought of the idea.
Adam Gary won't be here. …'s going to London.
Melanie Gary won't mind if we go ahead without ….
Don Are we going to have food?
Lisa … would be expensive to buy food for all the guests. Let's just ask … to bring something to drink.
Melanie Have we got any glasses?
Adam There are … in the kitchen cupboard. …'ll be all right. We can use ….
Don There won't be enough, but we can borrow ….
Adam We can't use my record player. There's something wrong with ….
Melanie What about a cassette recorder? Hasn't Daniel got … ?
Adam He had …, but he's sold ….
Don Who are we going to invite?
Lisa Who was that girl who came here on Friday?
Adam Rosemary.
Lisa Well, don't invite …. … wasn't very nice. I don't like … at all.
Melanie We all went to Margaret and Angela's party, so we ought to invite …. But let's talk about it tomorrow. I'm too tired tonight. …'s getting late.

Activity A

Imagine your class are giving a party. Discuss what you will need and where you can get it.

Activity B

Say which famous person you would most like to invite to dinner. Give a reason for your choice.

Object pronouns; possessive adjectives and pronouns

Some students are looking at an untidy pile of papers and other things. Complete what they say using these words: *me, you, him, her, us, them; my, your, his, her, our, their; mine, yours, his, hers, ours, theirs*.

1 **Sadie** This is Adam's ruler. It must be … because it's got … name on it.
   Gary I'll give it to ….
2 **Trevor** Are these gloves …, Rebecca?
   Rebecca Yes, they are. Thanks. They haven't got … name in them, but they belong to ….
3 **Alison** I think these notes belong to Lisa and Melanie. These pages are part of a project of ….
   Daniel I can't see … names on it, but I'll ask … about it.
4 **Gary** Adam and I have been looking for these magazines. Someone took them from … room. They belong to …. We're using the pictures for a project of ….
5 **Rebecca** Isn't this pen Emma's?
   Sadie I don't think it's one of …. I know she's lost … calculator, but I haven't heard … say she's lost a pen.
6 **Daniel** Is that book … ?
   Gary Yes, it's got … name in it, so it must belong to …. Here you are.
   Daniel Thanks, Gary.

Activity

Each of you puts one of your possessions on the teacher's desk. You then take it in turns to give one or two objects back to their owners. Ask e.g. *Whose is this? It is yours, Claudia? No, it doesn't belong to me. I think it's Bruno's*.

114 (BEG 20.8; 20.10)

Reflexive pronouns and **each other**

Angela goes to a club called Weight Losers. It's for people who want to lose weight. Angela is talking to a friend about the club. Put in a reflexive pronoun or *each other*.

Angela I go to Weight Losers now, you know. I'm trying to lose weight. I have to force ... to eat the right food. My husband doesn't think I'm fat. 'You'll make ... ill,' he tells me. But it's doing me good. Lots of people go to the club. They're all trying to lose weight or keep ... slim. We all weigh ... on the scales and write down our weight. Then the members all tell ... their weight. Yesterday one man was one kilo heavier than the week before. He said he couldn't stop ... eating cakes. The teacher says, 'You must control ..., all of you.' Helen goes too, you know. She's losing weight. She's very pleased with ... . The Johnsons were there yesterday too. They're always arguing with ... . They've lost a lot of weight, so they must be really starving ... .

Activity A

Have you ever tried to teach yourself a language? Discuss the advantages and disadvantages of learning without a teacher.

Activity B

Think of contexts for these sentences. Write four short paragraphs, each containing one of the sentences.

They blamed themselves for the accident.
They blamed each other for the accident.
Everyone helped themselves.
Everyone helped each other.

115 (BEG 20.8; 20.9)

Reflexive and emphatic pronouns

Complete this advertisement by putting in the reflexive and emphatic pronouns.

THE BIG BOOK OF DO-IT-YOURSELF
by Bill Hawk

Lots of people have already bought Bill Hawk's super new book. They've saved ... a lot of money by doing jobs ... . Here are a few examples.

Mr Purlin of Hamleigh repaired the roof of his house ... .

'We decorated the whole house ... . This book made it easy,' say the Cleat family of Huxton.

The Spriggs of Granby put in central heating ... . 'I asked ... : why not?' said Mr Sprigg. 'With Bill Hawk's help it wasn't very difficult.'

'I put in a new bath ... ,' says Mr Hunter of Milchester.

Mrs Flashing of Wayford says 'We wanted a garage. A friend said "Why don't you build it ... ?" He showed us the book. So we did it ... . Now we feel really pleased with ... .'

Mrs Stiles of Backworth fitted a new front door all by ... . 'I couldn't imagine ... doing anything like that until I read this book.'

Activity

Have you ever done any of these jobs yourself? Is Do-it-yourself popular in your country? Do you think it is a good idea? Discuss these questions with the other students.

one and ones

Wendy and Diane are shopping together in London. They're in a department store. Complete the conversation. Use phrases with *one* or *ones* to replace the phrases in brackets.

Wendy I need a new umbrella. I really must buy (an umbrella) soon.
Diane I saw (some nice umbrellas) in Bymore's when I was here last month.
Wendy I don't know the stores here very well. (Which store) is Bymore's?
Diane It's (the new store), (the store) opposite Harridge's.
Wendy Oh, yes, I know. Actually, Diane, I think your umbrella is (a very nice umbrella). Where did you get it?
Diane Oh, I've had (this umbrella) for a long time. I don't think you'll find (an umbrella) like this now.
Wendy They must have umbrellas in this store. I wonder which floor they're on.
Diane I think it's (this floor). Oh, yes, here they are.
Wendy I don't like (these brown umbrellas).
Diane (This umbrella) here is nice.
Wendy Well, I prefer (that umbrella) next to it, (the red umbrella). But it's rather big. I like (the umbrellas) that fold up very small.
Diane There's (an umbrella) here like that.
Wendy Yes, but I don't want (an umbrella) that colour.
Diane (Which umbrella) do you like best?
Wendy I don't really like any of them.
Diane I think (the umbrellas) in Bymore's were better. Shall we go there?
Wendy Yes, OK. Which way is the escalator?
Diane I think there's (an escalator) over there.

Activity A

Can you guess what *one/ones* refers to in these phrases? For example, if someone says *A long one or a short one?* They could be talking about a coat or a dress.

☐ A single one or a double one?
☐ Brown ones or white ones?
☐ The red ones or the green ones?
☐ An electric one or a manual one?

Activity B

Say which of these cars you would most like to have. Discuss your choice with the other members of the class.

117 (BEG 20.14)

some and any

Mrs Garland has bought a small house in the seaside town where she lives. She's going to let the house to tourists in summer. But first she needs to buy some things for the house. Look at Mrs Garland's list and say if the things she needs are in the sale.

Examples

There are some chairs in the sale.
There aren't any electric fires.

4 chairs	sofa
electric fire	shelves
2 beds	mirror
electric cooker	wallpaper
table	paint

BIG SALE

of furniture and household goods at the
Victoria Hall, Friday March 15th 7p.m.

Sofas, chairs, desks, cupboards, curtains,
carpets, mirrors, electric cookers, gas
heaters, kettles, wallpaper

Don't miss this wonderful chance to buy at
really low prices!

Activity

Does your classroom have everything you need to learn English? Say what there is in your classroom or in your school or college, e.g. *We've got some pictures on the wall, and there's a map of the USA. There aren't any travel posters.* What about a cassette recorder, readers, and so on? Try to think also of things you haven't got but think you ought to have.

118 (BEG 20.15; 20.16)

Quantifiers: every, each and any Compounds with every-, some-, any- and no-

Two teachers are taking a group of pupils on an activity holiday. They're about to leave.
Complete the conversation using *every* (×2), *each* (×2), *any* and compounds with *every-, some-, any-,* and *no-*.

Mr Blake All the luggage goes in the back. Put … in the back of the bus. And … piece of luggage must have the owner's name on it.
Michelle I've got … to eat here, look.
Mr Blake Yes, you can keep that with you.
Andrew Is it true we'll have to do written work … evening?
Mrs Walters Yes, it is.
Sharon I can't find a seat. There's … for me to sit.
Mr Blake Well, … seat has a number. Yours is ten.
Sharon Neil is sitting there. He says we can have … seat we like.
Mr Blake Well, he's wrong. He'll have to sit … else.
Mrs Walters I think we're ready now. There's … else to do before we go.
Simon There's … missing. Nick isn't here. We've looked … for him, but we can't find him … .
Mrs Walters Has … seen Nick?
Simon I've asked the others, but … knows … about him.
Mrs Walters Oh, it's all right. Here he is.
Mr Blake I hope … has been to the toilet. We don't want to stop … five minutes, do we?

Activity

Try to invent song titles using the words you put into the conversation, e.g. *Every time I look at you; I can't find her anywhere; Nothing will be the same again.*

Quantifiers: **a lot of, many, much, more, less** etc

The table on the right shows the amount of exports from Malrovia this year. Write sentences with *a lot of*, *many* and *much*.

Examples

They've sold a lot of oil.
They haven't sold many motor cars.

Then compare the amounts for this year with those for last year.

Examples

They've sold less oil this year than last year.
They've sold more motor cars.

Activity A

Look at this information on kettles. Compare the five kettles, e.g. *The Heatmaster holds quite a lot of water. It holds more than the Superboil. The Aqualux takes less time to boil than the Hotflow, and it doesn't cost as much.* Decide which kettle is the best value.

Kettle	Holds (litres)	Time taken to boil 1.5 litres	Price
Heatmaster	1.75	4 min. 15 sec.	£19.95
Superboil	1.5	4 min.	£22.25
Pronto	2.0	3 min. 35 sec.	£27.50
Hotflow	1.4	4 min.	£24.75
Aqualux	1.5	3 min. 45 sec.	£19.50

Exports

this year ■
last year □

Oil
Motor cars
Machines
Steel
Coal
Electrical goods
Clothes
Food

Activity B

Discuss with the other students how much money people in these jobs earn in your country: doctor, garage mechanic, policeman, shop assistant, lorry driver, secretary, bank manager, pilot. Write the jobs in order starting with the one that earns the most and ending with the one that earns the least. If there are students in your class from more than one country, then discuss the jobs in groups, and compare your lists.

120 (BEG 20.17; 20.19; 20.20)

too much, too many, some more, another and enough

Betty Root is the leader of the Forwards Party. She doesn't agree with the Prime Minister George Wright and his Progressive Party. Betty is talking on television. Complete what she says using *too many, too much, some more, another* and *enough*.

Mrs Root George Wright and his party have made far … mistakes during their time as the government. Mr Wright doesn't really spend … time at his job, I'm afraid. Our Prime Minister spends … time playing golf. While he's doing that, our industry is dying. A lot of factories have closed in the last few years – … factories, in my opinion. And we've just learnt that … factories are going to close soon, thanks to George Wright again. The Progressives simply don't spend … money on the really important things, like helping industry. And of course they spend … on things that no one needs. We don't want … Progressive government after this one. Mr Wright would like to give us … of the same medicine. But the medicine is killing our country. You gave the Progressives a chance to put the country right, and you've seen the result. Don't give them … chance.

Activity

Mention some of the problems facing the world today, such as hunger or nuclear weapons. Use *too many, enough* etc in some of your sentences.

121 (BEG 20.22; 20.23)

Quantifiers + of

Can you answer the questions in this geography quiz? Use *none, neither, one, two, three, both* or *all* in your answers.

Example

How many of these are rivers?
the Amazon, the Mississippi, the Nile
All of them are rivers.

1 How many of these are islands?
   Cuba, Florida, Mexico
2 How many of these are in Spain?
   Casablanca, Lisbon
3 How many of these are in South America?
   Angola, Bolivia, Colombia, Peru
4 How many of these are oceans?
   the Atlantic, the Pacific
5 How many of these are in London?
   Central Park, Hyde Park, Regent's Park
6 How many of these are in the USA?
   Chicago, Los Angeles, Miami, Philadelphia
7 How many of these are in Europe?
   The Dead Sea, Mount Everest, Lake Ontario
8 How many of these are in Australia?
   Adelaide, Melbourne

Activity

Invent some similar quiz questions and give them to a partner to answer. You could write questions about English vocabulary, e.g. *How many of these are food/clothes?* or about famous people, e.g. *How many of these are film stars/politicians?*

122 (BEG 21.1; 21.4)

Question words and question phrases

Martin's bicycle has been stolen. He's reporting it to the police. Complete the policeman's questions by putting in a question word or phrase.

Policeman	Martin
1 ...'s your name	Martin Wilkins.
2 ... do you live?	46 Elm Road, Granby.
3 And ... is the bicycle? ... owns it?	It's mine. I own it.
4 ... was it stolen?	This morning.
5 ... did you leave it?	Outside the town hall.
6 ... was this?	About eleven o'clock. When I came back at half past eleven, it wasn't there.
7 ... of bicycle is it?	It's a racing bike, a Silverman Special.
8 ... is it?	Blue.
9 ... is it?	It's two years old.
10 ... did it cost?	Oh, about £150.

Activity A

Act out the conversation with a partner, but invent some different answers. Imagine that your own bicycle, motor-bike or car has been stolen.

Activity B

Write a list of questions that the policeman might ask if someone reported that they had lost a lorry full of circus animals.

123 (BEG 21.2)

Asking about the subject and the object

Author Brenda Bagg has written a story called 'Heartache'. It's about a Lord who loves a film star who loves a pop singer and so on. The diagram shows who loves who. Brenda is showing the story to the film director Max Finkel. Give Max's questions and Brenda's answers.

Examples

Mike Perry →
Who does Mike Perry love? ~ Princess Flora.

→ Mike Perry
And who loves Mike Perry? ~ Jackie Logan and Sophie Salinsky.

1 → Princess Flora	5 → Lord Midwinter
2 Princess Flora →	6 → Sophie Salinsky
3 Peter Kane →	7 Sophie Salinsky →
4 Lord Midwinter →	8 Jackie Logan →

Activity

For each of these events write two different quiz questions. Ask a partner about each event.

☐ David killing Goliath
☐ Galileo inventing the telescope
☐ Wellington defeating Napoleon
☐ Leonardo da Vinci painting the Last Supper and the Mona Lisa

Try to invent similar questions to ask a partner.

124 (BEG 21.3)

who, what and which

Complete these riddles using *who, what* or *which*. You may first need to find the correct answer in the box below.

1 … goes up but never comes down?
2 … is paid money for taking something away from you?
3 … can go through a closed door?
4 … of these words is longer: 'laughs' or 'smiles'?
5 … has fingers but no arms?
6 … sheep eat more grass, black ones or white ones?
7 … invented the first pen?
8 … has more tails, one cat or no cat?
9 … is the difference between an African elephant and an Indian elephant?
10 … king of England wore the biggest shoes?

```
A hairdresser.
About 3,000 miles.
A pair of gloves.
The one with the biggest feet.
Your age.
The Incas. (ink-ers!)
A noise.
No cat. (No cat has more than one tail.)
White ones. There are more of them.
'Smiles' because there's a 'mile' between the first
and last letters.
```

Activity

Imagine that you have a friend who always stays at home in the evenings and never goes out. One day your friend tells you that he/she went out last night with someone to a cinema and then to a restaurant. What questions would you ask your friend?

125 (BEG 21.2; 21.5)

who asking about the subject; prepositions in questions

Mr Pratt is telling his psychiatrist about his dreams. Put in the psychiatrist's questions.

Examples

Mr Pratt I dreamt I was looking for something.
Psychiatrist *What were you looking for?*
Mr Pratt I don't know. Someone laughed at me.
Psychiatrist *Who laughed at you?*
Mr Pratt I couldn't see his face.

Mr Pratt I was waiting for someone.
Psychiatrist … ?
Mr Pratt I don't know. I was afraid of something.
Psychiatrist … ?
Mr Pratt I'm not sure. Somebody ran towards me.
Psychiatrist … ?
Mr Pratt A man I didn't know. Then I shouted at someone.
Psychiatrist … ?
Mr Pratt I think it was my brother. But then I fell over something.
Psychiatrist … ?
Mr Pratt Something lying in the road. Somebody was pointing at me.
Psychiatrist … ?
Mr Pratt My father. He was talking to someone.
Psychiatrist … ?
Mr Pratt I don't know. I woke up then.

Activity

A friend of yours has found a strange object in his garden. He thinks it is a space satellite. What questions might you ask him about it?

126 (BEG 22.2)

The relative pronouns **who** and **which**

'SF' is a radio programme about science fiction. The presenter is telling listeners about some new books. Look at the presenter's notes and give his sentences. Use a relative clause with *who* or *which*.

Examples

Tomorrow – A woman can see into the future.
'Tomorrow' is about a woman who can see into the future.

Into the Unknown – A spaceship loses its way.
'Into the Unknown' is about a spaceship which loses its way.

1 The Mind Machine – A computer controls people's thoughts.
2 Eureka! – A scientist discovers the secret of the universe.
3 Spaceville – Some people build a city in space.
4 Zero – An accident starts a nuclear war.
5 The President – A dictator rules the world.
6 Danger Hour – A cloud of gas pollutes the earth.
7 Starfight – A war breaks out in space.
8 Wait for Death – A man lives for a thousand years.

Activity

Do you like people who tell jokes all the time?
Do you like books which make you think? What about parties which go on all night? Write a few sentences about people and things you like or don't like. Then compare your sentences with a partner's.

127 (BEG 22.2–22.5)

Relative clauses

Find the right explanation for each of the twelve words below. Write a sentence with a relative clause to explain the meaning. Use *who, which* or *that*, or leave out the pronoun. (Sometimes there is more than one correct answer.)

Examples

A butcher is someone who sells meat.
A stamp is something you put on a letter.
Gloves are things that you wear on your hands.
A saucer is something you put a cup on.

1 socks	He/She sells fruit and vegetables.
2 a briefcase	You use them to row a boat.
3 a greengrocer	It heats water.
4 a present	You wear them on your feet.
5 a kettle	You try to hit it.
6 soap	You carry papers in it.
7 a target	It keeps the rain off you.
8 an artist	You give it to someone.
9 a seat	You can see yourself in it.
10 an umbrella	You sit on it.
11 oars	You wash with it.
12 a mirror	He/She paints pictures.

Activity A

Try to explain the meaning of these words: needle, mechanic, shampoo, sugar, brake, key.

Activity B

Ask the other students e.g. *What do you call a person who cuts your hair? What's a thing you cut wood with?* They have to find the answers.

Relative clauses without a pronoun: leaving out *who, which* or *that*

Last summer Amanda went on holiday with some friends. After she got back, she showed people the photos they had taken. Look at the photos and give Amanda's words. Use relative clauses without a pronoun.

Examples

Amanda and her friends stayed at this hotel. *'That's the hotel we stayed at.'*

They hired a car. *'That's the car we hired.'*

1 Amanda went with these friends.

2 They swam in this pool.

3 Amanda bought this dress. 4 They met these people.

5 They went for a sail in this boat. 6 They visited this castle.

7 They liked this beach. 8 They walked round this lake.

Activity

Have you got any photos of yourself visiting places? If you can, bring some photos to the lesson. Show them to a group of other students and explain what is in the photos.

129 (BEG 22.2–22.5; 22.8)

Relative clauses

Complete the conversation. Put in the relative clauses using the information in brackets. (Sometimes there is more than one correct answer.)

Example

She's the woman … (She lives in West Street.)
She's the woman who lives in West Street.

Diane I saw Roger Cowley on Saturday.
Paul Roger Cowley?
Diane Yes, he's the man … (He works at Electrobrit.)
Jane It's Roger Cowley … (His wife owns the Top Shop.)
Mark What's the Top Shop?
Jane It's the shop … (It sells dresses.)
It's the one … (I went in it yesterday.)
Mark Oh, I know. It was Roger Cowley … (His car was stolen from outside his house.)
Paul That's right. It was the car … (He bought it from Richard Hunter.)
Jane And who's Richard Hunter?
Mark I don't think you've met him. He's the man … (I invited him to our party.) He didn't come, though.
Jane Is he the man … ? (His sister was on a TV quiz show.)
Paul No, that's Bob. Richard is the man … (David plays golf with him.)
Diane Yes, but I was talking about Roger Cowley.

Activity

Write similar sentences about people you know. Use *who, which, that, whose* and a sentence without a relative pronoun.

130 (BEG 22.10; 22.11)

Relative clauses without a pronoun

Rewrite the advertising slogans using the infinitive, the -ing form or the -ed form.

Examples

The Ramplus 64 is the first computer that will fit in your pocket.
The Ramplus 64 is the first computer to fit in your pocket.

The person who uses a Fotax camera takes the best photos.
The person using a Fotax camera takes the best photos.

Clothes that are washed in Whizz look extra white.
Clothes washed in Whizz look extra white.

1 Food that is bought at Brisco costs you less.
2 Someone who listens to a Meditone radio hears every word.
3 Cakes which are made with Bakewell flour taste wonderful.
4 Hed-Cure is the only thing that will make your headache really better.
5 A person who is sitting in a Super-Plush chair is sitting comfortably.
6 The most exciting toy you can give your child is a Playworld toy.
7 Everyone notices the man who wears a Windsor shirt.
8 A floor that is covered with a Wonderlay carpet looks ten times better.

Activity

Write similar advertisements for these products: Amplex televisions, Glisso furniture polish, All-Night Stores.

Non-defining relative clauses

'Jubilee Road' is a weekly television programme telling a story of the lives of ordinary people. Every week the programme starts with a summary of what has been happening. The writer of this week's summary has left out some important information, which the programme editor has noted below. Rewrite the summary and put in the missing information. Use non-defining relative clauses with *who, whom, whose* and *which*. (Sometimes more than one answer is correct.)

Example

Laura, who hasn't been feeling well lately, has gone to see the doctor.

Activity

Read these sentences from a guide book to London.

> Sir Christopher Wren, who built 52 London churches, is best known for St Paul's Cathedral.
>
> The Post Office Tower, which was completed in 1964, is 189 metres high.
>
> Charles Dickens, whose house in Bloomsbury you can visit, was a famous novelist.

Write similar sentences about your home town or about a town you know well. Use non-defining relative clauses.

	Laura has gone to see the doctor.	*Laura hasn't been feeling well lately.*
1	Len is giving a big party.	*Len has finally found a new job.*
2	Craig is hoping that Donna will be at the party.	*Len has invited Craig.*
3	Craig also wants to borrow some money from Gordon.	*Gordon's cycle repair business is doing very well.*
4	The new club in Jubilee Road is very popular with young people.	*Everyone is talking about the new club.*
5	A disco kept people awake half the night.	*The disco took place at the club last weekend.*
6	The new manager at the plastics factory wants Donna to work late.	*No one likes the new manager.*
7	He has arranged a staff meeting.	*The meeting starts at ten o'clock tomorrow.*
8	Donna is staying at number 33 with Teresa.	*Teresa has given her the spare room.*
9	The woman at number 35 is behaving rather strangely.	*Donna spoke to the woman yesterday.*
10	Meanwhile Robin is explaining his problems to Harriet.	*Robin's wife has left him.*

The comparison of adjectives

A motoring magazine has tested six new cars and given them marks for price, running costs, reliability, and so on. The cars get up to 5 marks in each category. For example, 5 means very cheap, very economical etc, and 0 means not at all cheap or economical etc. 5 is the best mark and 0 is the worst.

Compare the cars using the notes on the right.

Examples

Prince/easy to drive/Delta
The Prince is easier to drive than the Delta.

Sahara/comfortable/Superior
The Sahara is just as comfortable as the Superior.

Swift/reliable/Libretto
The Swift is less reliable than the Libretto OR
The Swift isn't as reliable as the Libretto.

1 Superior/comfortable/Libretto
2 Swift/spacious/Sahara
3 Delta/cheap/Prince
4 Sahara/reliable/Libretto
5 Prince/comfortable/Swift
6 Delta/fast/Sahara
7 Superior/economical/Delta
8 Swift/easy to drive/Superior
9 Sahara/good-looking/Prince
10 Swift/comfortable/Libretto

Then write six sentences (11–16) saying which car is the best in each category.

Examples

The Sahara is the cheapest.
The Prince is the most economical.

	cheap	economical	reliable	easy to drive	comfortable	spacious	fast	good-looking
Prince	3	5	5	4	3	2	3	1
Delta	4	4	4	2	1	0	3	3
Swift	3	2	2	5	5	4	3	4
Sahara	5	3	4	2	4	3	1	3
Superior	1	0	3	4	4	4	5	5
Libretto	2	3	4	3	4	5	4	4

Activity A

Talk to your partner about your own car (or the car you would like to have). Discuss the similarities and differences between the two cars.

Activity B

Discuss the advantages and disadvantages of travelling by public transport as against using your own car or bicycle.

133 (BEG 23.2; 23.3)

The comparison of adjectives

Mike has the chance of a very good job in London. He and Wendy are discussing whether they should move from Milchester. Complete the conversation by putting in the comparative or superlative of each adjective in brackets.

Wendy I think we should go. You'll get a (high) salary with Multitech than you do now, and we'll have a (good) standard of living.
Mike Don't forget London is the (expensive) place we could possibly go to. For example, house prices are the (high) in the country. A house will be (difficult) to find there than in Milchester.
Wendy But it's probably the (big) chance you'll ever get. That's the (important) thing. And it'll be (easy) for me to find a good job than it was here.
Mike London is a (big) place than Milchester. Life won't be so quiet.
Wendy Well, I'd like a (exciting) life. It is a bit boring here sometimes. And it'll be much (convenient) for shops and theatres, living in London. You've never really liked your job here. And things have got (bad) recently.
Mike Yes, they have. And Multitech is certainly one of the (good) companies in the business. But I don't want to go unless you really want to.

Activity A

Say in what way these things are record breakers:
Everest, the Soviet Union, Antarctica, gold, football.

Activity B

Write a few sentences comparing town life and country life.

134 (BEG 23.6; 23.7)

Comparatives with **and** and with **the**

Samuel Tomani is a politician in Omagua. He's telling people how badly the government is doing. Look at his notes and give his sentences using the comparative patterns.

Examples

taxes high – hard to make a living
Taxes are getting higher and higher. The higher they become, the harder it is to make a living.

goverment corrupt – people bitter
The government is getting more and more corrupt. The more corrupt it becomes, the more bitter people are.

1 food expensive – people hungry
2 industry weak – our problems great
3 things bad – important to do something
4 people poor – our chances of success small
5 situation hopeless – difficult to put it right
6 people desperate – necessary to act

Activity

Write a few sentences on present-day political, economic or scientific developments. For example, you could mention nuclear weapons, food or computers.

135 (BEG 24.4)

The position of adverbs

Maria is writing to her friend Helen in England. She's rather tired, and she's left some of the words out by mistake. Rewrite the letter putting in the adverbs and adverb phrases on the right.

Dear Helen,

Thank you for your letter. Is it
four months since I last wrote?   really
I'm sorry, but I've been very
busy.   lately

I'm working for my exams.   already
I've planned my revision.   carefully
I work until about ten o'clock
in the evening.   usually
I've finished for today.   just

I don't keep to my   of course,
plan.   always
I saw a marvellous film.   yesterday
It was called 'The Secret Game'.
Have you seen it?

I don't go out.   actually, often
Suzanne comes about once a week.   here
We talk.   a lot

I hope to visit England again.   next year
I had a lovely time last year.   there
It would be great to see you.   again
I'm trying to save some money.   hard

How are you? Is your new flat
all right? Please write.   soon

Love,

Maria

Activity

The class divides into two teams. A student from Team 1 finds a sentence in an English book or newspaper. He/She writes the sentence on the board, leaving out one adverb or adverb phrase. He/She then writes the adverb on the board, under the sentence. Team 2 have to say where the adverb was in the sentence. They score two points if they guess exactly where it was, and they score one point for a correct position which is different from the original sentence. Then it's Team 2's turn to choose a sentence.

If this is too easy, find sentences with two adverbs or adverb phrases.

136　(BEG 24.5; 24.10)

Adverbs of manner

Mrs Lake is a teacher of English. She is making notes on her students. Say how well each student is doing at English. Use an adverb of manner in each sentence. (Most but not all of these adverbs end in -*ly*.)

Example

Ahmed: Bad spelling. Careless written work.
Ahmed spells badly. He does his written work carelessly.

1　Stella: Satisfactory progress. Good homework.
　　Stella is progressing …. She does ….
2　Emil: Fluent speaker of English. Wide reading.
3　Milena: Hard worker. Fast learner.
4　Victor: Slow speech. Incorrect pronunciation of some common words.

Activity A

Invent sentences which would be spoken in a certain manner, e.g. *We mustn't make a noise* or *Hurry up!* Your partner has to say how they are spoken, e.g. *quietly, impatiently.*

Activity B

One student thinks of an adverb (e.g. *quickly*) which he/she does not tell anyone. Ask the student to do different actions, e.g. *Clean the board. Walk across the room.* The student does these actions quickly (or happily, or carefully etc), and you guess the adverb by asking e.g. *Are you doing it quickly?*

137　(BEG 24.8)

Adverbs of degree

Robert Gorman is writing a guide to hotels in England. Here are his notes on the two main hotels in Milchester. Say how good the two hotels are.

		Grand Hotel	*Castle Hotel*
	comfortable?	+	0
	pleasant views?	0	+ +
1	good service?	+	+ +
2	good food?	0	+ +
3	clean?	+ +	0
4	quiet?	+	+ +
5	convenient?	+ +	+
6	reasonable prices?	0	+ +

+ + = very good
+ = fairly good　　0 = not very good

Examples

The Grand is fairly comfortable.
It's a bit more comfortable than the Castle.
The Castle isn't very comfortable.

The views at the Grand aren't very pleasant.
They're a lot less pleasant than at the Castle.
The views at the Castle are very pleasant.

Activity A

Is there a system of school and college marks or grades in your country? Do teachers give marks from 1 to 5 or a percentage mark? Explain the meaning of the different grades.

Activity B

Describe your country's climate. Say how hot or cold and how wet or dry it is, and so on, at different times of the year.

Adverbs of frequency

Amanda is looking for a boy-friend. The Find-a-Friend Club wants to help her. She's doing a personality test for them. Look at Amanda's answers and write sentences about her.

Examples

Amanda doesn't often lie awake at night.
She's sometimes angry.

Activity A

Say how often you do the things in the personality test.

Activity B

Discuss with a group of other students which television programmes you like. Say how often you and members of your family watch them.

How often do you do these things?	always	usually	often	sometimes	not often	never
lie awake at night					✓	
be angry				✓		
argue with people					✓	
worry			✓			
take risks						✓
be late for work	✓					
tell jokes					✓	
laugh at comedy shows		✓				
wish things were different			✓			
be sad					✓	

139 (BEG 24.12)

Adjective or adverb with a verb

Tom and Angela are at Lynn's party. Complete their conversation by choosing the correct adjective or adverb in the brackets.

Tom Well, the party is going very (nice/nicely), isn't it? Have one of these sausages. They taste (good/well).
Angela No, thanks.
Tom You don't sound very (happy/happily), Angela. And you look (pale/palely). Are you all right?
Angela I feel rather (tired/tiredly). And I'm (hot/hotly).
Tom It is getting a bit (warm/warmly) in here, isn't it? Well I can (easy/easily) open this window.
Angela Thanks. Actually, my head aches quite (bad/badly) too. I think it's (slow/slowly) getting worse.
Tom I'm (sure/surely) the music isn't helping. It seems rather (loud/loudly), doesn't it? Look, would you like me to take you home?
Angela No, it's all right, thanks. But if I could sit (quiet/quietly) somewhere for a few minutes, I might be OK.
Tom I'll ask Lynn if there's somewhere you can go.

Activity

Complete the sentences in your own words to form a paragraph. Use an adjective or adverb in each sentence.

Harry got up … . He felt … . His face in the mirror … . His voice … . His breakfast tasted … . He ate … . Everything seemed … .

140 (BEG 24.13; 24.14)

The comparative of adverbs

The Drama Club are rehearsing a new play. Jane is telling the actors what to do. They aren't doing things right yet. Complete what Jane says using the comparative of an adverb.

Examples

You didn't go out quietly enough, Mark. Can you go out *more quietly* next time?

You aren't near enough, Tom. Come *nearer* to her.

1 You have to speak really clearly. Can you speak … , please, Helen?
2 You didn't wait long enough, Lynn. Can you stay a little … in the doorway?
3 You haven't learnt your words very well, Peter. I hope you know them … next time.
4 You aren't angry enough, Sarah. Can you shout rather … ?
5 Angela, that isn't far enough. Walk … to the left.
6 And you're supposed to be nervous. Can you look round a bit … ?
7 I want you to hit the table hard. You can hit it … than that, Bob.
8 Be careful when you lay the table, Sue. Try to do it … next time.

Activity

Explain what these evening courses at Milchester College will teach you to do.

☐ Map-reading Made Easy
☐ Faster Typing
☐ More Fluent French
☐ Improve Your Cooking

Prepositions of place and movement

One of Brenda Bagg's stories is going to be made into a film. It's a romantic comedy about a girl who works in a baker's shop. The picture shows how Brenda imagines the scene at the start of the film. Complete her description of the scene for the film director. Put in some of these prepositions: *above, across, along, at, behind, between, by, from, in, inside, near, off, on, opposite, out of, outside, round, through, to, towards, under, up.* (Sometimes more than one answer is correct.)

Activity A

Describe your daily journey to school or work, giving full details of your route.

Activity B

Find a photo of an outdoor scene. (If possible, use a photo of your own.) Describe the photo using *on the right/left, in the foreground/background, next to* and other prepositions.

Activity C

Discuss possible methods of escaping from prison. These words may be useful: *cell, bars, rope, wall, ladder, tunnel, hide, gate, guard, disguise.*

Street scene. There are three shops. … the middle there is a baker's, which is … an antique shop and a toy shop. The toy shop is … the right. There is a phone box … the left … the corner of the street. A car is coming … the corner. There is a man on a bike … the car. There is also a car parked … the baker's. This car has a suitcase … its roof. A woman is just stepping … the pavement to walk … the road. She has come … the baker's. Two girls are standing … the baker's. A window cleaner is climbing … a ladder … the window … the toy shop. He has got a bucket … his hand. A woman is looking … the window. A boy is walking … the pavement … the ladder … the street corner. There is a man … the antique shop looking … an old telescope. There is a young man … the phone box, and three people are standing … the pavement waiting – a woman, a man and a boy. The boy is … the back of the queue.

Prepositions of time

Complete the news item about the British runner Stan Crowe. Put in the missing prepositions.

CROWE TO RUN AGAINST BOTO

Stan Crowe hopes to run against James Boto of Kenya in a 1500 metres race in Paris … June 16th. Both men will want to break Cliff Holding's world record. Holding ran the 1500 metres … 3 minutes 28 seconds last year. Holding will also be running in Seattle … June 14th, two days … the Paris meeting.

British fans have been hoping … several months to see Crowe win back his record. He last ran against Boto … April, when he fell and hurt himself … the race. He was just behind Boto … the time. The two men had not met … the last Olympic Games in Peking. Crowe has had to rest … his accident, but he was back in action … seven o'clock … Saturday evening when he won a rather slow race in Edinburgh. He hopes to be fully fit … the end of this month at the latest. If he is not fit for Paris, he will have to wait … the Commonwealth Games. These games take place in Ottawa … August 14th … the 20th.

Activity A

Explain when school holidays and public holidays occur in your country.

Activity B

Explain what the dates in brackets mean.

☐ William Shakespeare (1564–1616)
☐ Richard Nixon, US President (1969–73)
☐ The Bicentenary of American Independence (1976)

Activity C

Say what you do and how you feel before, during and after an important exam.

Prepositions

Complete this story of an (imaginary) person who spent three years alone on an island. Put in the missing prepositions.

… a Thursday evening … October 1931, … about eight o'clock, the ship 'Voyager' sank. The ship had been sailing … the end of September, when she left London, and was on her way … England … Australia. The only survivor was an Englishman called Wilfred Batty, who saved himself … swimming two miles. He spent three years … an island … the middle of the Indian Ocean.

The island was quite small, and he could walk … the whole of it … an hour. He climbed … the one hill and put a flag … it … a signal. … night Batty slept … a cave, where he felt quite … home. … the day, he often fished … a home-made net. He cooked the fish … a wood fire.

Batty stayed … the island … almost three years, … August 1934. A ship was sailing … the island, and the captain saw Batty's signal. The sailors found a man … a long blue coat … dark hair and a beard, looking rather … a gorilla. Batty was soon home, and a few years later he finally arrived in Australia … air.

Activity

Look at an English story and choose a paragraph with some prepositions in it. Copy the paragraph, leaving a blank instead of the prepositions. Then ask your partner to put in the prepositions.

144 (BEG 26.1; 26.2)

Phrasal verbs

Anthony Knight appears on the television programme 'Newswatch'. He asks important questions about people and things in the news. Complete his questions using these phrasal verbs:

blow up	(= explode)	go up	(= rise)
bring up	(= raise)	knock down	(= demolish)
come off	(= succeed)	put off	(= postpone)
find out	(= discover)	put up	(= increase)
get away	(= escape)	work out	(= calculate)

Examples

We've heard the government have postponed the decision. *Why have they put it off?*

The prisoners escaped, yes, but *how did they get away?*

1 Prices will rise. The question is, how much ... ?
2 Someone calculated these figures, but the government won't say who ... .
3 The Prime Minister says he's going to raise the question in Brussels, but when ... ?
4 We know the petrol tank exploded. Why ... ?
5 So the government are going to increase taxes. Well, how much ... ?
6 The Council say they're going to demolish the building, but why ... ?
7 The government say they discovered the mistake, but when ... ?
8 The plan succeeded. Why ... ?

Activity

Write a short news report about a meeting between the management and the trade union at the Electrobrit factory. Use these notes: ask/put up/wages–prices/go up–turn down/request–threaten/strike–go on/talk/all day–agree/put off/strike–both sides/think over.

145 (BEG 26.2; 26.3)

Phrasal verbs and prepositional verbs

Betty Root is talking on television. She doesn't agree with Prime Minister George Wright and his Progressive Party. Add a sentence about what happened when Betty was Prime Minister. Use *it* or *them* in the sentence.

Examples

Mr Wright hasn't carried out the national plan.
But we carried it out.

The Progressives haven't looked after old people.
We looked after them.

1 This government has closed down the universities. We didn't ... .
2 George Wright's government has put up income tax. We didn't ... .
3 The Progressives haven't listened to ordinary people. But we listened ... .
4 They've let down the country. We ... .
5 The Prime Minister has to look for excuses. But we didn't have to ... .
6 The Progressive government hasn't dealt with the unemployment problem. We ... .
7 They haven't kept down the cost of living. We ... .
8 They don't care about the people of this country. But we care ... .

Activity

Talk about your country's present government, what its ideas are and what it has done.

146 (BEG 27.2)

Clauses of time

Ten detectives work for Bymore's department store. Their job is to stop customers stealing things. Look at this note from the store manager and put in these conjunctions: *after, as, as soon as, before, since, until.*

To: All store detectives   **From**: Manager

Please remember these points.

1 It is important to act quickly. … you see a customer behaving suspiciously, inform the control team by radio.
2 Follow the customer … he moves around the store.
3 Do not speak to the customer inside the store. Wait … he has left the store.
4 … you have informed the control team, a second detective will join you to help with the arrest.
5 Arrest the customer outside and bring him to the control room for questioning. Do not question him … you get to the control room.
6 Remember that the control team have been filming the customer … you first informed them about him.

Activity

Frank Simlein is a writer of science fiction. He's writing a story about an American family called Mitchell who have survived a nuclear explosion and are living in an underground shelter. Suggest a few sentences with clauses of time that Frank might use.

147 (BEG 27.3)

Sub clauses with **that** and with question words

A man walked into a London hospital yesterday not knowing his own name. He'd lost his memory. Rewrite the man's words putting the main clause first and the sub clause second. Use a question word or *that.* (You can leave out *that* if you like.)

Examples

Who am I? No one knows.
No one knows who I am.

I'll get my memory back soon, I hope.
I hope that I'll get my memory back soon.

1 What's my name? I've no idea.
2 Where do I live? I don't know.
3 I'm a long way from home, I've got a feeling.
4 Why do I think so? I'm not sure.
5 Something strange has happened to me, I know.
6 How did it happen? I can't understand.
7 I just walked into the hospital, I've heard.
8 When did I come here? I can't remember.

Activity

Complete these sentences in your own words using sub clauses.

☐ I hope …
☐ I can never understand …
☐ I believe …
☐ I don't know …

148 (BEG 27.8; 27.9)

Clauses of reason and purpose: **because, to** and **so that**

Some people are saying why they are learning English. Give each person's reason.

Examples

Marcel I need it in my job.
Marcel is learning English because he needs it in his job.

Astrid I wanted to give myself a new interest.
Astrid is learning it to give herself a new interest.

Bruno I can use it when I travel.
Bruno is learning it so that he can use it when he travels.

1 **Ingrid** I like learning languages.
2 **Anita** I can help my daughter with her homework.
3 **Martin** I might need it some time.
4 **Claudia** I want to get a better job.
5 **Gaston** I'll be able to understand American films better.
6 **Andrea** I have to do it at school.
7 **Sven** I'll be able to read engineering textbooks in English.
8 **Jan** I want to impress my girl-friend.

Activity A

Make a list of things you would need in order to survive comfortably on a desert island. Say why you would need each one.

Activity B

Give as many reasons as you can think of why people want jobs.

149 (BEG 27.10; 27.11)

Clauses of result: **so** and **so/such** … **that** …

Last year the Cross family had a very disappointing holiday. Join each pair of sentences using *so* or *so/such … that …*. (You can leave out *that* if you like.)

Examples

They wanted a holiday. They looked at a Suntime brochure.
They wanted a holiday, so they looked at a Suntime brochure.

The holidays were very cheap. They booked one immediately.
The holidays were so cheap that they booked one immediately.

Alporta looked a very nice place. They decided to go there.
Alporta looked such a nice place that they decided to go there.

1 There was fog. Their flight was delayed.
2 The plane was very late. They got to bed at three in the morning.
3 It was a very long way to the beach. It took an hour from the hotel.
4 It was a very crowded beach. There was hardly room to sit down.
5 The hotel was very noisy. They couldn't sleep.
6 Their room had a very unpleasant view. It made them feel quite miserable.
7 They weren't enjoying themselves. They went home.
8 The holiday was very disappointing. They decided to ask for their money back.

Activity

Write similar sentences about an unsuccessful walk in the country.

Conjunctions and other linking words

Complete the short article on the bicycle as a form of transport. Put in these words or phrases: *after, also, although, because, but, but also, either, if, not only, on the other hand, or, so, that, when, whereas*. (Some of the words or phrases may be used more than once.)

The bicycle

Driving a car can be expensive. The bicycle, … , is a cheap form of transport. A bicycle … costs very little … lasts much longer than a car. It is … very cheap to use … of course it doesn't need any fuel. In fact, it costs practically nothing … you've bought it. It … helps keep you fit … you get exercise … you ride it. Another good thing about a bicycle is … it doesn't pollute the air. … everyone rode bicycles instead of driving cars, we wouldn't be using up the world's oil so quickly.

… the bicycle has these advantages, it has some disadvantages too. It is convenient only for relatively short journeys, … by car you can travel quite a long way in comfort. Another problem is … the cyclist is not protected from the weather and gets wet … it rains. Cycling isn't very nice in heavy traffic … . In Britain there are very few cycle paths, … bicycles have to share the road with cars and lorries. The best place for a bike ride is a quiet country lane. Main roads and city streets are often … busy … it needs some courage to take a bike on them. The cyclist has no protection, and … he is more likely than a motorist to be seriously hurt … killed … he does have an accident. Cycling keeps you healthy, … the cars may kill you!

Activity

Write a similar short article discussing the advantages and disadvantages of another form of transport such as the car, the train or the aeroplane.

151 (BEG 28.2)

The emphatic form of the verb

There were lots of things wrong with David's car, so he took it to Crook's Garage for repairs. But the garage didn't do the work properly, so David went back next day. Put in Mr Crook's sentences, using the emphatic form.

Examples

David You haven't done the work.
Mr Crook *We have done it. We did everything.*

David You didn't check the brakes.
Mr Crook *We did check them, you know.*

David The car doesn't feel safe.
Mr Crook It ... . There's nothing wrong with it.
David The lights don't work.
Mr Crook ... . We mended them.
David You didn't replace the front tyres.
Mr Crook ... . I remember doing it.
David The back doors won't open.
Mr Crook ..., you know.
David And the heater doesn't work.
Mr Crook ... . We checked it.
David But you didn't check the battery.
Mr Crook Yes, ... The battery is OK.
David Anyway, the bill isn't correct.
Mr Crook ... . I wrote it myself.
David You don't know what you're talking about.
Mr Crook ... . Repairing cars is our business.

Activity

Agree or disagree with these statements:

☐ Smoking doesn't do you any harm.
☐ Women can't do important jobs.
☐ Exams don't matter – learning is the important thing.

152 (BEG 28.4)

it + be used for emphasis

Police have arrested bank robber Hank Williams. They've promised to let him go if he gives them some information. He's telling them about the gang he belongs to. Look at the detective's notes and give Hank's words. Use *it* and *who/that*.

Examples

Williams joined the gang last March.
'It was last March that I joined the gang.'

Grabski organizes the bank raids.
'It's Grabski who organizes the bank raids.'

1 Bozo shot the policeman in Marseilles.
2 He went into hiding in Monaco.
3 Ross bought the guns.
4 They're planning to rob the Standard Bank next.
5 Gregory finds out all the inside information.
6 They're going to meet on Long Island next week.
7 Grabski intends to go to Morocco afterwards.
8 He's afraid of the Mafia.

Activity

Use the information below to write sentences about 'firsts'. Use *it* and *who/that*.

Example

It was in California that the first supermarket opened.

The first supermarket opened.	in 1914
the first President of the USA	Yuri Gagarin
The First World War began.	George Washington
the first person in space	in Greece
The First Olympic Games took place.	in California

Emphasis

Charlotte works for an advertising company. She's made some notes about a car called the Atlas. Rewrite each sentence in the way suggested in brackets, so that the underlined part has more emphasis.

Examples

An Atlas looks stylish. (do)
An Atlas does look stylish.

The Atlas gives you the best of modern technology. (it)
It's the Atlas that gives you the best of modern technology.

The Atlas is famous for its low petrol consumption. (what)
What the Atlas is famous for is its low petrol consumption.

1 The Atlas won the 'Road' magazine prize. (it)
2 It won the Monte Carlo rally last year. (do)
3 The Atlas gives you reliability. (what)
4 You have lots of room in an Atlas. (do)
5 The expert design makes you feel so comfortable. (it)
6 You'll never believe how much luggage it holds. (what)
7 The low price will really surprise you. (it)
8 The Atlas costs less than £7,000. (do)
9 You'll never want to let anyone else drive your Atlas. (what)
10 You ought to be driving an Atlas now. (what)

Activity

Write advertising slogans for these things. Give emphasis to your statements using *do, it* etc.

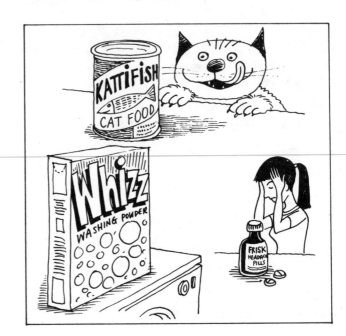

Key

An oblique stroke is used to indicate alternatives, and brackets indicate words which may be left out. For example, *He's washing the car/his car* means that *He's washing the car* and *He's washing his car* are both correct. *She's riding (a horse)* means that *She's riding* and *She's riding a horse* are both correct.

1

1 You must pay us £250,000.
2 The boy is safe.
3 He can go when we've got the money./When we've got the money, he can go.
4 He will be all right.
5 The money must be in £10 notes.
6 Bring the money to the car park.
7 Don't show this to the police.
8 If you talk to the police, you'll be sorry./You'll be sorry if you talk to the police.

2

Are we all here now?
Where's Tom?
He *isn't* here.
Oh, he *isn't* very well.
He's in bed.
And Sarah *isn't* here.
Oh, yes, I *am*.
Oh, there you *are*, over in the corner.
Angela's late.
Or *is* she ill, too?
No, she *isn't* ill.
Peter and Sue *aren't* here.
Yes, they *are*.
They're in the kitchen.
Am I late?
Yes, you *are*.
Oh, I'm sorry.
It's all right.
Here we *are*.
Now we're ready to start.

3

1 The garden is lovely.
2 The views to the north and east are beautiful.
3 The house has six bedrooms.
4 The rooms are large.
5 The downstairs rooms have carpets.
6 The sitting room has a lovely old fireplace.
7 The kitchen has plenty of cupboards.
8 The garage is big enough for three cars.

4

1 He's got a watch.
2 She's got a coat.
3 They've got a table.
4 He's got a (toy) car.
5 She's got some books.
6 They've got a television.
7 She's got a camera.
8 He's got a radio.

5

1 He's combing his hair.
2 She's reading the newspaper.
3 He's climbing a ladder.
4 They're carrying something.
5 She's washing her hands.
6 He's brushing his teeth.
7 They're playing cards.
8 She's eating an apple.

6

He *lives* in Belgravia in London's West End. He's very rich, and he *owns* the company Office Blocks International. Every morning the young Lord *has* breakfast in bed and *reads* the newspapers. He *gets* up at ten o'clock and usually *goes* for a walk in Hyde Park. He *has* lunch at his club. He sometimes *meets* the Directors of OBI, and they *talk* about the company's plans. In the afternoon Lord Stonebury and his friends sometimes *play* golf. Then they *have* a few drinks. Or sometimes he and a girl-friend *go* for a drive in his sports car. After dinner Lord Stonebury *goes* to a night club or a casino with one of his girl-friends. They *get* home at about two o'clock. In the winter the young Lord *lives* in Monte Carlo. And he *spends* his summer holidays in the West Indies.

7

She doesn't play computer games.
She likes music.
She often visits people.
She doesn't like sport.
She doesn't go swimming.
She doesn't like animals.
She goes for walks.
She doesn't often go out in the evenings.

8

Brenda, where *do you get* your ideas for all your stories?
Does it take a long time to write a book?
Do you write every day?
And *where do you work*?
Do you type your stories?
Does your husband *like/read* your stories?
Where does your husband *work,/What does* your husband *do*, Brenda?
Why do so many people *read* your books, Brenda?

Key

9

Milchester *is* a lovely old town on the River Swenley. The famous castle *brings* lots of tourists to the town. The old streets near the castle *have* many interesting little shops, and there *is* a very good museum. The town also *has* a theatre and a cinema. 27,000 people *live* in Milchester, and quite a few of them *work* at the new computer factory. Other industries *are* paper-making and chocolate.

10

1 Brian builds houses. He's washing the car/his car at the moment.
2 Alice teaches music. She's swimming at the moment.
3 Maureen and Jackie make dresses. They're playing tennis at the moment.
4 Alan drives a lorry/drives lorries. He's eating a banana at the moment.
5 Stephen plays golf. He's watching television/TV at the moment.
6 Jessica reads the news. She's reading a book at the moment.
7 Tony and Roger sell cars. They're jogging at the moment.
8 Miranda takes photos/photographs. She's riding (a horse) at the moment.

11

Greetings from Wales! Ben and I *are doing* something different this year. We're at the North Wales Activity Centre. People *come* here every summer to learn more about their hobbies and interests. I'*m doing* photography and tennis this week and Ben *is learning* about computers. We *get* up at half past eight every morning and *do* lessons from ten to half past twelve. We *have* lunch at one, and then there are more lessons. So it's hard work. But I *like* it here. We'*re having* a super time. It's half past seven in the evening now, and we'*re sitting* out on the grass in front of the Centre. The weather is good. See you soon. Love, Kate.

12

I hear there *was* a barbecue at the college last Saturday. *Were* you there?
Yes, I *was*. Where *were* you?
Oh, I *wasn't* here on Saturday. I *was* in London.
That's a pity. It *was* a very good barbecue. The food *was* great.
What *was* the weather like here?
Oh, we *were* very lucky with the weather. It *was* nice and warm.
Were there a lot of people there?
Yes, lots. Lynn *wasn't* there, though. She *wasn't* very well.
What about Mark and Jane?
Oh, they *were* still on holiday last Saturday, so they *weren't* at the barbecue. But all the others *were* there.

13

What happened? Where *were* you? And where *was* the monster?
I *was* here on the beach. I saw the monster in the water. Then it swam out to sea. It *was* a great shock. It *wasn't* very nice, I can tell you.
What *was* the monster like?
Big. It *was* a very large animal. It *had* a large body, but it *had* a small head. Its eyes *were* blue and round. It *had* teeth, but they *weren't* very big. It *didn't have* any ears.
Did you take a photo of it?
I *didn't have/hadn't got* my camera with me, I'm afraid. And it *was* very quick. It all happened in a moment.

14

Picasso painted pictures.
Billie-Jean King played tennis.
Neil Armstrong went to the moon.
Marco Polo travelled to China.
Martin Luther King worked for Black people's rights.
Christian Dior made clothes.
Columbus sailed to America.
Edison invented the electric light.

15

1 A car *stopped* outside the shop, and two men *got* out.
2 They *had* masks on.
3 One of them *held* a brick in his hand.
4 He *threw* the brick at the window and *smashed* it.
5 One man *took* the coats from the window, and the other *put* them in the back of the car.
6 It all *happened* very quickly. People just *stood* and *watched*.
7 The men *jumped* into the car and *drove* away.
8 I *ran* to a phone box and *called* the police.

16

He didn't repair the broken window.
He didn't book a holiday/his holiday.
He wrote to the bank/his bank.
He didn't phone the sports club.
He paid the electricity bill/his electricity bill.
He tidied the garage.
He didn't paint the gate.
He didn't clean the windows.

17

1 Why did you disappear?
2 Did you leave the country?
3 How did you travel?
4 Did your friends hide you?
5 What did you do in all that time?
6 Did you read the stories about you in the newspapers?

7 Why did you come home?
8 Did your husband find you?

18

1 Bob has repaired the fence.
2 Philip and Mark have decorated the club room.
3 Angela has bought some new curtains.
4 David has polished the cups.
5 Martin has serviced the minibus.
6 Paul and Sarah have laid a new carpet in the bar.
7 Mike and Helen have cleaned out the kitchen/have cleaned the kitchen out.
8 Tom has put up some more shelves/has put some more shelves up.

19

He's made a pop record. He made one in 1965.
He's walked to the South Pole. He walked to it/walked there in 1952.
He's climbed Everest. He climbed it in 1959.
He's run a marathon. He ran one in 1955.
He's won the Monte Carlo rally. He won it in 1962.
He's swum the English Channel. He swam it in 1950.
He's flown an aeroplane. He flew one in 1974.
He's met the Queen. He met her in 1980.

20

Hello, Bob.
Hello. I *haven't seen* you for a long time.
I *saw* you in town two or three weeks ago, but you *didn't see* me. I *was* on a bus.
Well, how are things? Are you still living over the shop?
No, I'*ve moved* now. I *found* a super flat just before I went on holiday. I'*ve been* there three months.
Have you *passed* your driving test yet?
Yes, I have. I *passed* in October. I *haven't bought* a car yet, though. But what about you, Bob? *Has* anything exciting *happened* to you lately?
No, not really. My mother *hasn't been* very well for a few months now.
Oh, dear. I'm sorry to hear that.
And my brother's out of work.
Did he *leave* school in the summer, then?
Yes. He *didn't do* very well in his exams and he *hasn't found* a job yet.
Are you still working at Scott's?
Yes. They'*ve* just *given* me a pay rise.
Well, that's one piece of good news.

21

1 After the bank clerk had looked at my cheque, she counted out the money.
   After she had counted out the money, she gave it to me.

2 After the tourists had got out of the coach, they took photos.
   After they had taken photos, they got back in the coach.
3 After the reporter had gone to the scene of the accident, she interviewed the people there.
   After she had interviewed the people there, she wrote a report on the accident.
4 After the mechanic had taken the wheel off the car, he put a new tyre on.
   After he had put a new tyre on, he put the wheel back on.

22

1 I was walking across a bridge when I met a tiger.
2 The roof fell in when we were watching television.
3 I was climbing the stairs when I saw a ghost.
4 I was looking into the mirror/a mirror when it broke.
5 The wind blew me over the cliff/a cliff when I was walking along a path.
6 We were lying on the beach when an elephant came out of the sea.
7 I was digging the garden when I found a dead body.

23

Melanie has been washing up for half an hour.
Sadie and Adam have been tidying up for an hour and a half/for one and a half hours.
Lisa has been looking for a bucket for ten minutes.
Alison and Jason have been working in the garden for three hours.
Don has been cleaning the stairs for half an hour.
Emma has been repairing the toaster for an hour.
Trevor has been mending the door bell for twenty minutes.
Daniel and Rebecca have been brushing carpets for two hours.

24

Manchester United manager Brian Price *has gone* to Turin for talks with the Juventus club about Wayne Simmonds. Simmonds *joined* Juventus a year ago, and he *has scored* 18 goals for them. Last autumn he *was scoring*/he *scored* almost every week, but he *has not been playing*/he *has not played* well recently. English fans would welcome his return, and yesterday everyone at United *was talking* about Simmonds. In fact, the club *has been waiting* for some time now for a chance to talk to the player.

At the moment Simmonds is England's greatest footballer, although he *has been* in the game for only two years. He *was playing* amateur football for Mendip Athletic when Bristol City *invited* him to join them. When Arsenal *bought* Simmonds for £750,000, he *had spent* only six months with the Bristol club, but he *had already played* twice for England Under-21s. Simmonds quickly *became* a big star, and he *has now played* five games for the full England team, although he *has played* only one game since he *left* Arsenal for Juventus.

25

1 The accident *happened* at 10.47 pm on October 23rd at the corner of Compton St and Brooks Rd, Milchester.
2 Mr and Mrs Johnson *were* on their way home. Mr Johnson *was driving*.
3 The couple *had been visiting* friends. They *had been drinking*, but Mr Johnson *had had*/Mr Johnson *had* only one small whisky. He *had finished*/He *finished* this drink at 10.15 pm.
4 It *was not raining* at the time, but it *had been raining*/it *had rained* shortly before, and the roads *were* wet.
5 At 10.47 pm Mr Richard Hunter *was cycling* north along Brooks Rd. He *had* his lights on.
6 Mr Johnson *did not stop* at the 'Stop' sign. As he *was turning*/he *turned* into Brooks Rd, he *hit* Mr Hunter and *knocked* him off his bike.
7 Mr Hunter *was* not badly hurt, but his bike *was* damaged. Mr Johnson *stopped* and *reported* the accident.
8 Mr Johnson *has been driving* for twenty years now. He *has not had* an accident before.

26

How long *have* you *been living*/*have* you *lived* in this house, Mrs Vincent?
I*'ve been living*/I*'ve lived* here for seventy-five years now.
And how long is it since your husband *died*?
Oh, he*'s been* dead for forty years. Yes, he *died* a long time ago. I*'ve been* alone since then. It*'s been* a long time.
And where *did* you *live*/*did* you *use to live* before you *came* here?
Well, before we *got* married I *lived*/I *used to live* with my parents in William Street. They*'ve knocked* the house down now. I*'ve only lived* in two houses all my life.
I expect you*'ve seen* a lot of changes in all that time.
Oh, yes. Milchester *was*/*used to be* very quiet in my young days. And it *wasn't*/it *didn't use to be* as big as it is today. I *used to go* for picnics on Long Hill with my brothers and sisters. Now they*'ve built* houses there.
Did you *enjoy*/*Did* you *use to enjoy* life in those days?
Oh, yes. We *had*/We *used to have* a wonderful time. People *were*/People *used to be* a lot friendlier in those days. We *did*/We *used to do* things together. Nowadays people just sit at home and watch television, don't they?

27

Robots will do all the hard work.
There won't be/There will not be so many jobs.
People will have more free time.
The weather will be colder.
There won't be/There will not be very much oil.

There will be fish farms under the sea.
People will fly to other planets.
People won't be/will not be very happy.

28

1 Neil is going to look for an outdoor job.
2 Michelle and Kevin are going to do electronics.
3 Sharon is going to become a taxi driver.
4 Simon is going to take a course in banking.
5 Nick and Julie are going to stay at school another year.
6 Adrian is going to work for the family business.
7 Tina is going to train to be a social worker.
8 Ian and Jeremy are going to hitch-hike round the world.

29

1 We're going to put in new escalators. They'll move people around more quickly.
2 We're going to employ more assistants. They'll help our customers.
3 We're going to put in cameras. They'll stop people stealing things.
4 We're going to play music. It'll produce the right atmosphere.
5 We're going to have televisions. They'll inform customers about things in the store.
6 We're going to have a children's room. Parents will be able to leave their children there.

30

Someone told me you and the family *are going to* go and live in Alaska. Is it true?
Yes, it is. I*'m going to* work for a building company.
That*'ll* be interesting.
I hope so. It*'ll* be something different. It*'ll* certainly be/It*'s* certainly *going to* be a lot colder than London.
When *are* you *going to* leave?
On the tenth of next month. We*'ll* be/We *shall* be there in three weeks.
Oh, so it *won't* be long now. Jerry and I *will* be sad to see you go.
Oh, we*'ll* be/we *shall* be back some time. We *won't* be/We *shan't* be/We *aren't going to* be there for ever. And you can always come to Alaska and see us.
Well, that isn't a bad idea. We*'re going to* visit my sister in Vancouver next summer.
Oh, that's great. We*'ll* see/We *shall* see you next summer then.

31

On Tuesday he leaves Madrid at 7.40 and arrives in Athens at 13.55. He is visiting the Ramplus offices.
On Wednesday he leaves Athens at 8.15 and arrives in Milan at 12.35. He is opening a/the new Ramplus factory.

On Thursday he leaves Milan at 10.10 and arrives in Strasbourg at 11.15. He is meeting the President of the Common Market.

On Friday he leaves Strasbourg at 10.45 and arrives in the Hague at 11.40. He is having discussions with the Dutch Minister of Technology.

On Saturday he leaves the Hague at 9.30 and arrives in Stockholm at 12.25. He is going to the Computer Show.

32

1 World leaders *are to* meet next month.
2 A dock strike *is starting* tomorrow.
3 The Prime Minister *is to* visit Greece in August.
4 The Queen *is leaving* for Australia tomorrow.
5 Some Chinese tourists *are arriving* in Britain next Saturday.
6 A shoe factory *is to* close.
7 The European Games *are to* take place next year.
8 Three new players *are joining* Liverpool.

33

1 You *will be* on holiday soon. In two weeks from now you *will be lying* on a beach.
2 You *will have* a good life, and you *will live* a long time.
3 Your personality is changing all the time. In ten years time you *will have changed* completely.
4 At some time in your life you *will have* a bad accident, but you *will not die*.
5 You *will marry* when you are twenty-three.
6 In twenty years from now you *will be living* on the other side of the world. By that time you *will have left* your husband.
7 You *will be* rich. When you are thirty-five, you *will already have made/will already be making* a lot of money.
8 At this time of your life you *will be working* very hard. Your life *will be* very exciting.

34

Where *are* you and Ben *going* for your holidays/*are* you and Ben *going to go* for your holidays, Kate?
Morocco. We'*re spending*/We'*re going to spend* ten days in Agadir.
Oh, that'*ll be*/that *will be* nice. When *are* you *going*?/When *do* you *go*?
On Friday night. Our plane *leaves* at seven, and we *arrive*/we'*ll be arriving* at four in the morning.
You'*ll need*/You'*re going to need* a holiday after that.
Oh, I don't mind night flights. Anyway, we'*ll be enjoying* the sunshine this time next week.
Are you *staying*/*Will* you *be staying* in a hotel?
Yes, a big hotel not far from the beach.
Our holiday *isn't* until next month. Jerry and I *are going to tour* Scotland in the car, we've decided. We'*re going to do*/We'*ll be doing* some walking, too. The weather *won't be* like/*isn't going to be* like Agadir, of course.

How long *are* you *going* for?
Two weeks. We haven't been to Scotland before, so it'*ll be*/it *will be* something different.
Are you *going to take*/*Are* you *taking*/*Will* you *be taking*/*Will* you *take* your caravan?
No, we don't want to take the caravan. We'*ll have to*/We *shall have to* find hotels to stay in as we go.
Well, we'*ll be*/we *shall be* back from Morocco before you go. Have a nice time, Kate.

35

Mr and Mrs Stokes *were* sitting in the garden of their Bristol home when I arrived to interview them and their fourteen-year-old son Carl. But Carl *was* working upstairs. 'He *doesn't* often leave his room,' his mother explained.

At the moment Carl *is* working on a programme for a new computer game. Computers *have* become his whole life. In the last year Carl *has* earned over £25,000 from writing programmes. A lot of other people *are* trying to do the same nowadays, but not many of them *have* done as well as Carl.

'When *did* he buy the computer?' I wondered. 'We bought it for him eighteen months ago for his birthday,' said Mr Stokes. 'We *didn't* know what we *were* doing. Our son *has* changed. Eighteen months ago he *hadn't* seen a computer. Now he *doesn't* talk about anything else. And we *don't* understand a thing about computers.' 'And *do* you think it's good for him?' was my next question. 'No, we *don't*. We worry about him,' said Mrs Stokes. 'He *doesn't* have any other interests now. And he *hasn't* done any work for his school exams. It's often quite a job to make him go to school at all.'

Carl's parents *don't* understand computers, but Carl certainly *does*. 'I love computers,' he said. 'I soon got tired of playing games, though. I like writing programmes much better. I've got three computers now. I bought two more. I *didn't* earn much at first, but now I *do*. My parents make me put most of it in the bank.'

36

It'll be wet. There'll be strong winds.
It'll be dry most of the time. It'll be windy.
There'll be some rain in places. It'll be sunny at times.
It'll be warm. There'll be some sunshine.

37

Hello, Mike. *Did* you *have* a nice time in France?
Hello, Paul. Yes, we did, thanks. We *didn't have* very good weather, but we still *had* a good time.
Have you already *had* your lunch?
Yes, I was early today. And I only *had* a sandwich.
You can *have* one of my sausages if you like.

109

No, thanks. I'*m* only *having* light lunches this week. I'm trying to lose weight.
You haven't got anything to worry about.
You're going camping in Wales next week, aren't you?
That's right.
I hope you *have* nice weather.
So do I. Did you know Mark and Jane are in Benidorm at the moment? We *had* a postcard from them on Friday. They say they'*re having* a marvellous time.
I took some photos in France. You can *have* a look at them some time if you like.
OK.
Come round to our house tonight, and we can *have* a talk.

38

Friday
We couldn't sleep/weren't able to sleep because it was so hot. We could hear the noise of insects all night.
Saturday
We were able to get water from a stream. We could see some smoke to the south.
Sunday
We couldn't travel/weren't able to travel because it was so wet. We were able to keep dry.
Monday
We were able to walk several miles along the bank of a river. We couldn't cross/weren't able to cross the river because it was so wide.
Tuesday
We were able to kill and eat a monkey. We could hear a plane somewhere above us.
Wednesday
We couldn't walk/weren't able to walk because we were so ill. We were able to sleep for several hours.

39

1 Psycho-Clinic is wonderful. My problem was that I *couldn't* fly/*wasn't able to* fly. I was afraid of aeroplanes. As soon as my course was over, I *was able to* take a flight to the Canary Islands! I had a super holiday. Now I *can* fly where I like. Next summer I'*ll be able to* go/I *can* go to the West Indies. (I *won't be able to* do/I *can't* do that every year because I haven't enough money.) I *can't* thank Psycho-Clinic enough.
2 Now at last I *can* stand up in front of a group of people! From now on my life will be different. I'*ll be able to* do my job much better in future. I often have to give talks to sales people at work. I just *can't* avoid it. In the old days I *couldn't* sleep/I *wasn't able to* sleep for a week before a talk. I *could* hardly do my work. But now I *can* give a talk without feeling too nervous. Last week I *was able to* get a good night's sleep before talking to a group of twenty people the next day. It's marvellous!

3 Yesterday someone asked me for my telephone number, and for the first time in my life I *was able to* give the number without looking in my book. Before I went to Psycho-Clinic I always forgot numbers and names. I *couldn't* remember/I *wasn't able to* remember them at all. Now, thanks to Psycho-Clinic, I *can* remember much more. If I see someone in the street tomorrow, I won't need to hide—I'*ll be able to* stop/I *can* stop and say hello to them.
4 I didn't like crowds of people. I *couldn't* go/I *wasn't able to* go to the theatre or the cinema. I love horse racing, and I *couldn't* go/I *wasn't able to* go to the races. But the people at Psycho-Clinic *were able to* stop me feeling afraid. Now I *can* do all those things. Yesterday I *was able to* stand in a crowd at a baseball game. I'*ll be able to* lead/I *can* lead a normal life now. There's an interesting show at the local theatre next week, and I'*ll be able to* see it.

40

In Britain you'*re allowed to* drive a car when you're seventeen. You *have to* get a special two-year driving licence before you can start. When you're learning, someone with a full licence always *has to* be in the car with you because you *aren't allowed to* take the car on the road alone. You *don't have to* go to a driving school—a friend can teach you. The person with you *isn't allowed to* take money for the lesson unless he's got a teacher's licence.

Before you'*re allowed to* have a full licence, you *have to* take a driving test. You can take a test in your own car, but it *has to* be fit for the road. In the test you *have to* drive round for about half an hour and then answer a few questions. If you don't pass the test, you'*re allowed to* take it again a few weeks later if you want to. In 1970 a woman passed her fortieth test after 212 driving lessons! When you've passed your test, you *don't have to* take it again, and you'*re allowed to* go on driving as long as you like, provided you are fit. Britain's oldest driver was a Norfolk man who drove in 1974 at the age of 100.

Before 1904 everyone *was allowed to* drive, even children. Then from 1904 motorists *had to* have a licence. But they *didn't have to* take a test until 1935. In the early days of motoring, before 1878, cars *weren't allowed to* go faster than four miles an hour, and someone *had to* walk in front of the car with a red flag.

41

1 We aren't allowed to light fires.
2 We aren't allowed to play ball games.
3 We have to leave before ten o'clock in the morning.
4 We don't have to worry about food.
5 We weren't allowed to light fires.
6 We weren't allowed to play ball games.
7 We had to leave before ten o'clock in the morning.
8 We didn't have to worry about food.

9 We won't be allowed to light fires.
10 We won't be allowed to play ball games.
11 We'll have to leave before ten o'clock in the morning.
12 We won't have to worry about food.

42

1 You must turn right.
2 You mustn't smoke.
3 You must stop.
4 You must go straight on.
5 You mustn't turn round.
6 You mustn't take photos.
7 You must turn left.
8 You mustn't go faster than fifty miles/kilometres an hour.
9 You mustn't overtake.

43

Well, I'm going to give you some medicine. You *must* take it four times a day before meals. And go on taking it even if you feel better. You *mustn't* stop taking it until you've finished the bottle. You *must* drink all of it. Now, you *must* stay in bed today. It's the best place for you at the moment. You can get up tomorrow if you like. You *needn't* stay in bed all the time when you start to feel better. But you *mustn't* go outside this week. It's too cold. And you really *mustn't* do any work at all. You need absolute rest. You *must* just relax for a few days. You can eat a little if you like, but you *needn't* if you don't want to. But don't forget to keep drinking. You *must* drink as much water as you can. You'll probably be all right again next week, so you *needn't* call me again unless you feel worse. But I'm sure the worst is over.

44

1 The pills ought to be in a safe place. The baby might eat them.
2 There oughtn't to be a hole in the carpet. Someone might fall over.
3 The towel oughtn't to be over the cooker. It might catch fire.
4 The drawer ought to be shut. It might fall out.
5 There oughtn't to be (any) broken glass on the floor. Someone might step on it.
6 There ought to be a plug on the kettle. Someone might get an electric shock.

45

1 She would walk. She wouldn't swim.
2 She would keep it. She wouldn't take it to the police.
3 She would listen. She wouldn't move to another seat.
4 She would choose the well paid job. She wouldn't choose the interesting job.
5 She would say no. She wouldn't say yes.
6 She would drive on. She wouldn't stop.

46

1 Four across. Past tense of 'be'.
    It could be 'was' or 'were'.
    It can't be 'were'. It must be 'was'.
2 Six across. It carries things by road.
    It could be 'van' or 'lorry'.
    It can't be 'van'. It must be 'lorry'.
3 One down. Person learning something.
    It could be 'student' or 'pupil'.
    It can't be 'student'. It must be 'pupil'.
4 Two down. Opposite of 'old'.
    It could be 'new' or 'young'.
    It can't be 'young'. It must be 'new'.
5 Three down. You pay to ride through the streets in it.
    It could be 'bus' or 'taxi'.
    It can't be 'taxi'. It must be 'bus'.
6 Five down. Planes travel in it.
    It could be 'sky' or 'air'.
    It can't be 'sky'. It must be 'air'.

47

What's the matter? Why have you stopped?
There's something wrong. It isn't going properly.
Let's have a look.
We *could* be/*might* be out of petrol, I suppose.
We *can't* be out of petrol. We only got some half an hour ago.
Well, if there is something wrong, *can* you/*could* you put it right, do you think?
Give me a chance. I don't know what the trouble is yet.
Look at this steam. The engine *must* be too hot.
Don't take the cap off the radiator. You *mustn't*/ You *shouldn't*/You *oughtn't to* do that. You *might*/You *could*/You'*ll* get boiling water all over you.
If it's too hot, we'*ll* have to wait until it cools down.
And how long *will* that take?
We *ought to*/We *should* wait about half an hour before we go on.
I suppose there *might* be/*could* be something else wrong with it.
We passed a garage about a mile back. I suppose they'*ll* come/they *might* come and have a look at it if we ask them.
The car *should* be/*ought to* be all right. Our local garage has just serviced it. I paid £30 for a full service.
You *needn't* worry. I'm sure it's just got too hot. Let's wait a bit.
We'*ll* be/We *shall* be late now, I expect.
There's some coffee in the back of the car. *Shall* we have some while we're waiting? There are some sandwiches, too.
I'm starving. I *must* have/I'*ll* have something to eat.
Would you like a sandwich, Lisa?
No, thanks. I *mustn't*/ I *can't* eat bread. I'm on a diet.

We *must* phone/*ought to* phone/*should* phone Matthew if we're going to be late.

We *won't* be very late, I don't think.

You *ought to* buy/*should* buy a new car, Adam.

Well, it *would* be nice if I had the money. But I'm afraid we'*ll* have to/we *shall* have to put up with this old thing for a little longer.

48

Hello, Sadie. Aren't you doing any work? You *ought to be revising* for the exams.

I *would be reading*/I *might be reading* my notes if I had them, but I've lost them.

Good Lord! How awful! Do you want to look at mine?

No, thanks. It's OK. Don't worry, Emma. Exams aren't important.

Not important! You *must be joking*! I'*d be looking* everywhere if my notes were lost.

Well, I'll probably find them before tomorrow.

Have you seen Lisa? She's got a book of mine.

She was in here not long ago. Perhaps she's outside. She *might be sitting* in the garden.

I'll go and have a look. Then I *must be going*/I *ought to be going*. I have to get to the library before it closes.

What are you doing tonight, Emma?

Revising, of course. Aren't you?

I *might be playing* tennis with Rebecca. If the weather stays fine, that is. It'll be too late for revision tonight.

49

1 She shouldn't have touched it.
2 The murderer must have been one of the five people in the house.
3 He shouldn't have told anyone about it.
4 The murderer might have taken it.
5 She couldn't have walked to the study.
6 She might have killed him.
7 He couldn't have taken it.
8 He must have been in London.

50

Where's Harry, then? I *can't* see him.

Yes, we said seventeen hours. He *should* be/He *ought to* be here by now.

He might not *be able to* find the place. He *might*/He *may*/He *could* have crossed the border in the wrong place.

Impossible! Harry *couldn't* have/*can't* have made a mistake. You know Harry.

Well, I hope he comes soon.

It's the most important job he's ever done for us. He absolutely *must* get the information.

I've often wondered about Harry. You don't think he *might* be/*could* be working for the other side?

No, I don't. Harry is one of us.

Well, I just think this job has been easy for him so far. Too easy. Perhaps the Omaguans know all about Harry. Someone *might* have/*may* have/*could* have told them about the job. They *might*/They *may*/They *could* have a man in our organization.

I don't believe it. They're not clever enough. But Harry is clever.

But you *can't* be sure. What if it was true?

It *would* be the end for us, of course. But it isn't true.

Harry takes a lot of risks. He does dangerous things. The boss lets him do what he wants. Harry shouldn't *be allowed to* put other people in danger. I told the boss, but he didn't listen. He *should* have/He *ought to* have listened to me.

Shut up, will you? Harry is a good man. Only Harry *could* do/*can* do this job.

It's seventeen oh two. We're late.

You're right. We *must* go/*ought to* go/*should* go at once. We *mustn't*/We *can't*/We *oughtn't to*/We *shouldn't* stay here any longer.

We've waited and he hasn't come. We *needn't* have driven here at all.

We had to be here. Harry *might* have/*could* have come. He *would* have done if he'd been able to.

Just a minute. There's someone behind that tree. Two men, I think. They *must* be watching us. Why else *would* they/*could* they be here?

Right. Have your gun ready. We may *have to* shoot our way out.

OK, I'm ready.

Let's go then. Come on!

The car *won't* start! Oh, my God! Where's my gun? Give me my gun!

Put your hands up. Get out of the car! Lie down!

It was you, Oskar! You told the Omaguans about Harry, didn't you? You *must* be mad. Oh, my God!

51

Betty Root would be a good Prime Minister. People should vote for her.

They *shouldn't vote* for her, you mean. She'd be no good. George Wright's party is the best.

It *isn't the best*, you know. Betty Root's party is the best. Her people have got the right ideas.

They haven't got the right ideas at all. Remember what happened when Root was Prime Minister? She made mistakes.

She didn't make mistakes. She did well. She took the right decisions.

I'm afraid *she didn't take the right decisions*.

Things were OK in Betty Root's time.

They weren't OK (in Betty Root's time), you know. They were terrible.

Betty understands our problems.
She doesn't understand our problems. But George Wright does. He's been a good Prime Minister.
He hasn't been a good Prime Minister. He's been awful.
George is popular. People like him.
They don't like him, I tell you. They're tired of him.
George Wright will win.
He won't win. Betty Root will. I'm sure of that.

52

Think back to half past six this evening, Lennie. *Where were you?*
Where was I? I don't know. I was walking somewhere. Yes, I went for a walk.
Do you often go for walks?
No, not often, but I did tonight.
Did you go to Dixie's wine bar?
No, I didn't go to Dixie's wine bar.
Have you got a car?
Yes, of course I've got a car. It's a Mavis Corona.
What colour is it?
Blue. Look, *why are you asking me all these questions?*
I'm asking you all these questions because there's been a robbery. Now, the number of the car. *Do you know it?*
No, I don't know it. I can't remember numbers.
Well, I can help you. I think it's BDX 25S. *Am I right?*
Well, you *may* be right. I'm not sure.
Did you steal the car?
No, I didn't. I never steal.
I'm very interested in your car, Lennie. *Where is it?*
I don't know. I've no idea where it is. Someone's borrowed it.
Well, *who's borrowed it?*
A man I know.
Can you remember his name?
No, I can't. I can never remember names.
You forget names too, do you? Well, let's talk about your walk. *Where did you go?*
I went to the park.
Did anyone see you?
No, no one saw me. Well, I don't *think* anyone saw me.
Did you see anyone you know?
No, I didn't see anyone I know.
Are you going to tell me the truth, Lennie?
What do you mean — am I going to tell you the truth? I'm telling it *now.*
You went out for a walk! No one saw you!
Well, *someone* saw me. I've just remembered.
Who was it?
It was a policeman. He's called Phil Grady. He spoke to me in the park. I know him well — he's arrested me twice.
What time was this?
Oh, about half past six, I think.
Just a minute. I'm going to make a phone call.

53

1 Why aren't Puffco/Puffco's tankers serviced until they break down?
2 Why had the driver been on the road for nine hours?
3 Why wasn't the warning sign put up again?
4 Why are lorries allowed to go as fast as they like?
5 Why haven't the police taken any notice of the villagers?
6 Why hasn't a by-pass been built?
7 Why do Puffco/Puffco's drivers still use the route?
8 Why haven't we learned any lessons from past accidents?

54

Hello. You're Wendy, *aren't you?*
Yes. I remember you, too. You're Roger Cowley.
That's right. We were in the same class, *weren't we?* But it's easy to forget people, *isn't it?*
I think I remember most of the people here. Jessica Squires is over there. She reads the news on Television North-West, *doesn't she?*
Yes, she's on television quite often. She's done well, *hasn't she?*
We had a lot of fun at school, *didn't we?*
Er, yes. Don't turn round, but Malone's looking this way. Mike Malone.
Yes, you can remember him, *can't you?*
Oh, yes.
I hated him. Oh, no! He's coming over here.
Well, it is a reunion. We ought to be friendly, *oughtn't we?*
Hello, Roger. Nice to see you again.
Nice to see you too, Mike.
This reunion was a good idea, *wasn't it?*
Yes, I'm enjoying it. Mike, do you remember Wendy?
Yes. She's my wife.
Oh!

55

Did you see Holland and Mexico on television last night?
Yes, it was a great game, *wasn't it?* Holland were marvellous.
They won't find it so easy against Poland, *will they?*
No, they won't. Poland have got a good team, *haven't they?*
Lobak looks good, *doesn't he?* The Austrians couldn't stop him, *could they?*
It'll be an interesting game, *won't it?*
England haven't been very good, *have they?*
Luck hasn't been on our side, *has it?*
But why is Bodger playing? He isn't very good, *is he?*
He didn't play very well against Peru, *did he?*
He doesn't play as well now as he used to, *does he?*
Well, we should beat Nigeria, *shouldn't we?*
I don't know. Anything could happen, *couldn't it?*
The West Germans are good, *aren't they?* They don't take any risks, *do they?*

They're playing Hungary tonight. You'll be watching, *won't you*?
Yes, of course.

56

1 The Prince and the Delta don't look good, but the Swift does.
2 The Prince and the Delta can't do 150 kilometres an hour, but the Swift can.
3 The Prince and the Swift don't use less than 10 litres of petrol per 100 kilometres, but the Delta does.
4 The Prince and the Delta are cheap to repair, but the Swift isn't.
5 The Prince and the Swift have got four doors, but the Delta hasn't.
6 The Prince hasn't got much room/a lot of room inside, but the Delta and the Swift have.
7 The Prince won a 'Road' magazine prize last year, but the Delta and the Swift didn't.
8 The Prince is good value, but the Delta and the Swift aren't.
9 The Prince doesn't look (very) good, and neither does the Delta.
10 The Prince can't do 150 kilometres an hour, and neither can the Delta.
11 The Prince doesn't use less than 10 litres of petrol per 100 kilometres, and neither does the Swift.
12 The Prince is cheap to repair, and so is the Delta.
13 The Prince has got four doors, and so has the Swift.
14 The Delta has got a lot of room inside, and so has the Swift.
15 The Delta didn't win a 'Road' magazine prize last year, and neither did the Swift.
16 The Delta isn't very good value, and neither is the Swift.

57

I hope this party's good.
I hope so, too. I don't know how we're going to get there.
Is the car still out of action?
I'm afraid so.
What's the matter with it?
I'm not sure, but I think it's something electrical.
Haven't you taken it to the garage yet?
I'm afraid not. I haven't had time.
Well, Martin will be going, won't he? We can ask him for a lift.
Yes, *I suppose so.* I don't imagine there's a bus.
I don't expect so. Not in the evening.
OK, I'll ring Martin. He might be taking Richard, of course.
Oh, *I hope not.* That man talks about horse racing the whole time. He's so boring.
Yes, *I know.*
Do we have to take a bottle to this party?
No, *I don't think so.* Tony didn't say.
We'd better take some wine. There's a bottle in the cupboard.

58

1 Polinski won the long jump and McCall the high jump.
2 Ivor Ketapov won't be running in the 100 metres, but/and no one knows why (he won't).
3 He holds the 200 metres world record but not the 100 metres (world record).
4 British runners have broken records, but British swimmers haven't/but not British swimmers.
5 A Frenchman is leading in the marathon and a Swede in the cycle race.
6 There were big crowds on Tuesday but not on Wednesday.

59

It's the English exam in two weeks. Have you done any work for it?
No, I'm afraid not/I'm afraid I haven't. I haven't had much time lately.
Neither have I./Nor have I./I haven't either. I've been very busy.
I've been to all the classes, though. And I've done the homework.
I haven't. I always have so many other things to do in the evenings.
There's an oral exam, isn't there?
Yes, I think so/I think there is. Mrs Moss mentioned it last week in one of our lessons.
I can do written work all right *but not oral work.*
Oh, nonsense. Your spoken English is very good. You can hold conversations in English, can't you?
Yes, I suppose so./I suppose I can. Perhaps I'll do all right. Are we allowed to use dictionaries in the exam, do you know?
I don't think so/I don't think we are. Why don't you ask Mrs Moss?
Yes, I will. She'll know, won't she?
I expect so./I expect she will.
I really must pass the exam.
Will you need English in your job?
I'll need it to get a good job.
So will I./I will, too. But don't worry, Ahmed. Your English is fine. You're going to pass.
Well, I hope so./I hope I'm going to. I know *you* will.
I wish I could be so sure. I'm certainly not looking forward to it.
Neither am I./Nor am I./I'm not either. I'll be glad when it's over, in fact.
So will I./I will, too.

60

1 The post box is emptied.
2 The stamps are postmarked at the post office.
3 The letters are sorted into the different towns.
4 The mail is loaded into the train.

5   The mail bags are unloaded after their journey.
6   The bags are taken to the post office.
7   The letters are sorted into the different streets.
8   The letters are delivered.

61

The warship Mary Rose *was built* in the years 1509–10. In 1544 England *started* a war against France, and in 1545 French ships *were sent* across the Channel towards England. Some English ships *went* out from Portsmouth to meet them. One of these ships was the Mary Rose. It was carrying 91 guns and 700 men — twice as many as normal. It *sank* quickly to the bottom of the sea even before it *was attacked* by the French. About 650 men *died*. This terrible accident *was seen* by the king of England himself.

The next month an attempt *was made* to raise the Mary Rose, but it *failed*. The ship *was forgotten* for hundreds of years.

In the 1970s new plans *were made* to raise the ship. Thousands of objects *were brought* up from the ship by divers. Then, on 1st October 1982, the Mary Rose *was lifted* out of the sea. Many people *saw* the raising of the ship on television. Finally the Mary Rose *was taken* into Portsmouth dock 437 years after she had sunk.

62

1   It was won by Italy.
2   They were written by Georges Simenon.
3   He was killed by James Earl Ray.
4   It was invented by John Logie Baird.
5   They were built by the Egyptians.
6   It was directed by Attenborough.
7   They were spoken by Hamlet.
8   He was played by Sean Connery.

63

1   A man has been killed in a motorway accident.
2   The Olympic Games have begun.
3   Some children have been injured in a gas explosion.
4   A picture has been stolen from a museum.
5   Charles and Diana have arrived in India.
6   Some secret papers have been lost.
7   A famous house has been sold to an American.
8   Ray Jenks has won an important race.
9   A dead body has been found in a park.
10 Fifty 'Style' shops have been bought by the Wilson-McArthur group.

64

1   (Some) photos are being taken.
2   (Some) footprints are being measured.
3   The area is being searched.

4   Someone is being questioned.
5   (Some) notes are being taken.
6   A call is being made.

65

1   Costs have to be reduced.
2   The factory must be kept open.
3   Action must be taken.
4   The staff should be warned.
5   Things ought to be made clear to them.
6   No more new staff will be employed.
7   The situation cannot/can't be allowed to continue.
8   The next meeting will be held on May 8th.

66

The world's first electronic computer *was built* at the University of Pennsylvania in 1946, although computer-like machines *had been built/were built* in the 19th century. Computers *were sold* commercially for the first time in the 1950s, and a lot of progress *has been made* since then. Computers are now much smaller and more powerful, and they *can be bought* much more cheaply.

Computers *are used/have been used* in many fields — in business, science, medicine and education, for example. They *can be used* to forecast the weather or to control robots which make cars. The computer's memory is the place where information *is kept* and calculations *are done*.

A computer cannot think for itself — it *must be told* exactly what to do. A lot of difficult calculations *can be done* very quickly on a computer.

And computers don't make mistakes. Stories *are heard/have been heard* sometimes about computers paying people too much money or sending them bills for things they didn't buy. These mistakes *are made* by the programmers — the people who give the computer its instructions. Some years ago, a computer-controlled rocket belonging to the USA went out of control and *had to be destroyed*. The accident *was caused/had been caused* by a small mistake in one line of the programme. This mistake cost the USA $18 million.

Criminals have found out that 'computer crimes' are often a lot easier than robbing banks. Hundreds of millions of dollars *are stolen* from American businesses every year by people changing the information in computers.

Large numbers of home computers *have been sold* recently, especially in the USA and Britain. People know more about computers than they used to, and computers are playing a bigger part in our lives. Progress *is being made* all the time. Many people believe we can look forward to the day when even our household jobs like cleaning *are done/will be done* by computer-controlled robots.

Key

67

1 The tennis player Kathy Duprey was given £50,000 for winning a competition.
2 £40,000 has been paid to the skier Anne Stolberg to advertise ski trousers.
3 The ice hockey team Phoenix Flyers was given/were given $20,000 each to play in front of the cameras.
4 £250 is paid to (the) footballer Wayne Simmonds for every goal he scores.
5 The cyclist Luigi Delgado was offered £25,000 to advertise a soft drink.
6 The boxer Howard Duke will be paid $3 million for his next fight.
7 A holiday in the West Indies has been promised to the London Wonders basketball team if they win the league.

68

They'll need to have the garage wall re-built.
They can replace the broken glass themselves.
They'll need to have a new floor laid in the dining-room.
They'll need to have the bedroom ceiling repaired.
They'll need to have a new kitchen window put in.
They can paint the outside of the house themselves.
They can decorate all the rooms themselves.
They'll need to have the electrical wiring checked.

69

1 If you choose a Sunspot holiday, you'll have a great time.
2 You'll sleep a lot better if you sleep in a Dreamway bed.
3 People will notice you if you wear Rodeo jeans.
4 If you shop at Kwikbuy, you'll save money.
5 If you use Luxidor Paint, your house will look beautiful.
6 You'll know what's happening if you read the Daily Talk.
7 If you wash with Whizz, your clothes will be cleaner.
8 If you drive a Delta, you won't want to drive any other car.

70

1 If the pay was good, I could afford a nicer flat.
2 If my boss didn't give me so much work, I wouldn't have to stay late.
3 If his writing wasn't so awful, I could read it.
4 If he listened to me, I wouldn't have to tell him everything twice.
5 If the offices weren't such a long way from here, I wouldn't spend so much time on the bus.
6 If there were some cafés nearby, I wouldn't have to take sandwiches.

71

Miss Lester, what is the situation in Omagua?
Well, it's very bad. Thousands of people have died, and thousands more *will die* soon if they *don't get* help. The people have very little food or water. And if we *don't do* something soon, things *will get* much worse. There will simply be nothing left to eat.
Is the British government doing anything to help? If they *sent* food, that *would help* to save lives, wouldn't it? After all, Omagua was once a British colony.
Yes, indeed. And the country is very poor, of course. But our government refuses to do anything quickly. They say they need time to find out about the problem. But we haven't got any time. It *will be* too late if they *don't do* something soon.
Well, it doesn't look as if Omagua is going to get any help for the moment. So what next? What *will happen* if the country *doesn't get* enough food or enough money to buy food?
Well, if our government *isn't* willing to help, we'*ll have to* ask people to send us money. In fact, we're asking them now.
How much are you asking people to give?
We're asking them just to send what they can. Even small amounts will be welcome. We'*ll be*/We'*d be* very grateful if people *send/sent* what they can afford. After all, if everyone in the country *gave* just 10p, we'*d have* a lot of money, wouldn't we? I'm sure if people *knew* exactly what things were like in Omagua, they'*d want* to help.
And are you hopeful that people will send money?
Oh, yes. If people *hear* about the problem, as they're doing now, then they'*ll help*, I'm sure. They always have done before.
Is there still time to get food and money to the people who need it, Miss Lester?
Oh, yes. We'll put the money to good use immediately. If people *post* money to us tomorrow, the food *will be* in Omagua by the end of the week.
Well, it's certainly a good thing that you're able to help the Omaguans. If your organization *didn't exist*, things *would be* much less hopeful. Now, can you tell us the address where people should send money? . . .

72

Gary and Emma wouldn't have got wet if they had had their anoraks.
If they hadn't forgotten to bring a map, they wouldn't have lost the way.
They wouldn't have been late if they had gone the right way.
They would have been able to eat at the café if it hadn't been closed.
If they had had some food with them, they wouldn't have been hungry.
If Alison hadn't fallen and hurt her leg, they wouldn't have had to go more slowly.
They wouldn't have missed their bus home if they hadn't got to Raveley so late.
If Adam hadn't been at home, he wouldn't have been able to come and fetch them in his car.

73

I think a new road is a good idea. It'*ll keep* the traffic out of the town if they build a by-pass. The traffic in the High Street is terrible. If they'd had any sense, they'*d have built* a by-pass years ago.

But what about the shopkeepers? If there was a by-pass, then people *wouldn't stop* here. And there'll be fewer customers in the shops if there'*s* less traffic in the town.

I don't agree. I think more people *will want* to shop here if it's quieter and pleasanter.

Tourists *won't come* into the town if there's a by-pass.

If the High Street *was* less busy, it would be a lot easier to cross the road.

There'*d be* less noise if there were fewer heavy lorries.

And the traffic doesn't do the buildings any good. Everything shakes when a heavy lorry goes past. Do you remember those old houses in West Street? They had to knock them down because of damage by lorries. If there'*d been* a new road ten years ago, they *wouldn't have had to* do that. And cyclists have been knocked off their bikes by lorries. One man was killed. That *wouldn't have happened* if the lorries hadn't had to use the High Street.

Don't forget that if you *improve* the road system, then the traffic may simply increase. Or you'll just move the problem to another town.

But look at the situation now — dozens of lorries moving very slowly through the town. It *would save* a lot of time if they travelled more quickly along a by-pass.

The by-pass would use up good farmland that we can't afford to lose.

The route goes right through Gordon Bentley's farm. It'*ll cut* his farm in two if they build it there. He only bought the farm three years ago.

Well, if that *happened*, they'd pay him for the land.

He told me yesterday he *wouldn't have bought* the farm in the first place if he'*d known.*

But a by-pass is for the whole town.

Well, if I *was* Gordon, I'*d be* angry about it.

I'm angry now about the traffic in the High Street. If they *don't give* us a by-pass, there'll be trouble, I can tell you.

74

If you've got a job to do, it always takes longer than you think.

If you're in an accident, it's the other person's fault.

If you want to buy something, they usually don't make it any more.

If you're absolutely sure about something, you're probably wrong.

If you type your own letters, they're usually short.

If you try to make a difficult situation better, you usually make it worse.

75

1 It says he will have lots of energy, and he may have to travel.
2 It says she will have problems at work, and she should ask her friends for help.
3 It says he will meet someone interesting, and his life may change suddenly.
4 It says they are feeling rather unhappy, but they will hear some interesting news.
5 It says her life is getting more exciting, but she must control her feelings.
6 It says he is worrying a lot, but his problems aren't very great.
7 It says her life feels empty, but she will find romance.
8 It says her boss or teacher will not be pleased with her, but it won't be her fault.
9 It says he should spend more time with his friends because he is working too hard.
10 It says everything is going well for them, but they must think before they make any decisions.

76

1 News Extra said (that) Arnold Motors had never paid any tax.
2 Newsday Magazine said (that) Arnold spent the company's money at a Las Vegas casino.
3 International News said (that) when he died, he would probably leave more than $500 million.
4 Modern World said (that) Stanley Arnold never spoke to his children.
5 The Daily Free Press said (that) he was planning to leave his money to a dogs' home.
6 World Magazine said (that) Arnold had friends in the Mafia.
7 The Saturday Reporter said (that) the police ought to ask Stanley Arnold some questions.
8 The Daily Talk said (that) no one would be sorry when he'd gone.

77

1 They asked me if/whether I had/I've got a car.
2 They asked me if/whether I could drive/I can drive.
3 They asked me where I went/where I'd gone to school.
4 They asked me what exams I took/I'd taken.
5 They asked me what I knew/I know about animals.
6 They asked me if/whether I liked/I like animals.
7 They asked me why I wanted/I want the job.
8 They asked me if/whether I was/I'm willing to work on Saturdays.

78

She asked me why I shopped/I shop there, and I told her I shopped/I shop there because it was/it's cheap.

She asked me if/whether I could/I can get everything I wanted/I want at Brisco, and I told her I couldn't/I can't get good bread.

She asked me how far away my home was/is, and I told her it was/it's one mile away.

She asked me if/whether I had come/gone there by car, and I told her I had.

She asked me how much I had just spent, and I told her I'd (just) spent about £15.

She asked me if/whether I'd come/go to Brisco again, and I told her I would.

79

They asked us not to park in the centre of Milchester.
They told us to show our tickets.
They told us to wear our numbers on our shirts.
They asked us to wear running shoes.
They told us not to carry any bags or bottles during the run.
They told us to follow the correct route.
They asked us to run on the left.
They asked us not to leave litter.

80

1 Mr Crane said that lots of people used/use the buses.
2 Mrs Manston asked how they could/can get to town.
3 Mr Budge replied that most people in the village had a car/ have (got) a car.
4 The chairman told everyone to keep quiet and listen.
5 Mrs Davies asked what was going to/what's going to happen to the school bus.
6 Mr Budge answered that it would/will continue to run.
7 Mr Rice said that the village needed/needs a bus service.
8 Mr Budge wondered·if/whether the villagers could/can start their own service.
9 Mr Hepplestone asked everyone to protest to the government.

81

1 The Silonians have refused to give away Bingozi.
2 The Magundians have promised to give full rights to Silonians in Bingozi.
3 The Silonians have advised the Magundians to think again.
4 The Magundians have suggested meeting for discussions.
5 The Silonians have warned the Magundians to expect trouble.
6 The Magundians have invited the Silonians (to come/to go) to Magundi to discuss the problem.
7 The Silonians have threatened to start a war (if the Magundians do not leave Bingozi).
8 The Magundians insist on looking after their people in Bingozi.

82

He wishes he could find work.
He wishes he hadn't left school when he was twelve.
He wishes he'd had a real job.
He wishes his health was good/better.
He wishes he had (some) friends.
He wishes people liked him.
He wishes the children weren't afraid of him.
He wishes he hadn't got into trouble with the police.
He wishes he'd known his parents.
He wishes he hadn't had (such) a bad start in life.

83

It's time we *found* Givens, isn't it? And we've still no idea where he is. The way things are going, it'll be Christmas before we *catch* him.

I wish Maxley Prison *had looked* after him a bit better last week.

If they'*d discovered* the escape more quickly, we'd have had a better chance of getting him.

And now we haven't got enough men. If we *had* more men, we'd probably find him.

We don't even know where his girl-friend is.

If only we *knew* where she lives now. I bet he's with her. We'll get him in the end.

I wish they *hadn't let* him escape in the first place.

When we finally *find* him, he'll probably have a gun.

Of course. So we'll just have to be careful. He won't have a chance if he *tries* to shoot his way out.

84

1 Have you got a lawn to mow? It's easier to mow it with a Swish machine.
2 Have you got some shoes to clean? It's best to clean them with Gleem polish.
3 Have you got a dirty job to do? It's sensible to do it in Atkinson's work clothes.
4 Have you got some luggage to take? It's easier to take it in a car like an Alton Sahara.
5 Have you got a dog to feed? It's better to feed him/it Chomp.
6 Have you got a sum to do? It's quicker to do it with a Numerex calculator.

85

1 Bill makes them work very hard.
2 He forces them to take the game seriously.
3 Bill wants the players to feel proud of the club.
4 Bill teaches them to play well together.
5 He makes them watch films of other teams.
6 Bill lets them relax after a game.
7 The club expects the players to behave.
8 Bill doesn't allow them to go to night-clubs.

9 The fans want the team to do well.
10 The fans would like the club to win everything.
11 Bill invites schoolboys to visit the club.
12 The chairman has persuaded local companies to give money to the club.

86

1 The group were forced to go with the guerrillas.
2 They were made to walk fifty miles to the guerrilla camp.
3 Miss Lester wasn't allowed to send a message to anyone.
4 She was made to carry a heavy bag.
5 The group were expected to look after injured guerrillas.
6 They were allowed to move around the camp.
7 They were allowed to talk to each other.
8 Miss Lester was warned not to try to escape.

87

It's been impossible for her to feel at home here.
Will it take long for the boss to give us a definite decision?
I've arranged for the psychologist to see Kelly on Friday.
We'll have to wait for her to write her report.
There isn't any reason for us to keep her here any longer.
It's quite usual for children to be in here for months.
It would be a mistake for everything to happen in a big hurry.
It's important for the children here to know about our plans for them.

88

1 They didn't know how to get the spaceship back.
2 They couldn't think where to look.
3 They weren't sure whether to wait in the street.
4 They had no idea where to go.
5 They didn't know whether to hide.
6 They had no idea how to contact Chupron.
7 They weren't sure whether to go to the police.
8 They didn't know what to think.

89

Are you still working for Electrobrit, Nigel?
No, I'm not. I'm afraid I lost my job there. And Polly's lost her job too. We're having rather a difficult time at the moment.
Oh, dear. I'm sorry *to hear* that.
I've been out of work for six months now. I expected *to find* a new job fairly quickly, but it isn't so easy, I've discovered. Jobs are hard *to find* these days.
With Polly not working we've very little money *to spend*. After I lost my job I managed *to make* my bank manager *lend* us some money, but he won't let us *borrow* any more now. And there are lots of bills *to pay*. I really don't know what *to do*.
Do you think you might *find* a job if you moved somewhere else?
Well, perhaps. We've talked about it of course. We've even wondered whether *to go* abroad. We could always *make* a

fresh start in a different country. Polly wants me *to look* for a job in America. And I've written to Australia House, although I'm still waiting for them *to answer*.
Do you like the idea of living abroad?
I don't know really. I think on the whole I'd rather *stay* here if I had a job. But the situation has made us *think* carefully about our future. We decided we ought *to find* out what opportunities there are. I've agreed *to think* about all the possibilities.
Well, I hope you find something soon.
I simply must *find* a job soon, or I don't know what we shall *do*.
Well, let me *know* what happens, won't you? Look, here's my new address and phone number. Give me a ring some time.
OK, David. I'd better *go* now. I've got a bus *to catch*.
I hope *to see* you again soon.
'Bye, David.

90

Racing driver Chuck Loder, who had a bad accident in last year's Grand Prix, is likely *to be coming* out of hospital soon. He agreed *to be interviewed* by our sports reporter, although he has refused *to be photographed*, as his face still shows the marks of the accident.

Chuck was very cheerful when he spoke to us. His health now seems *to be improving* slowly. He expects *to be sitting* at the wheel once again before very long.

Many people think that last year's race at Bruckheim ought never *to have taken* place. It was the last race on the old track, which is going *to be re-built* soon. The owners of the track expect *to have completed* the work in time for next season.

Chuck hopes *to be driving* in next year's Grand Prix. We wish him luck. Read his personal story of the Bruckheim accident in next week's Daily Talk.

91

2 (horse) riding
3 fishing
4 camping
5 skiing
6 sailing
7 climbing
8 (ice) skating

92

She left the Polytechnic without taking any exams.
Elaine decided to see the world before making her home in Britain.
She thought about her career while filling shelves in a supermarket.
On returning to Britain, Ms Archer bought a small food store.
She made her stores a success by pleasing the customers.
She has risen to be head of the company in spite of being a woman in a man's world.

93

Mike's not much good around the house. Do you get any help from Paul?
Yes, he doesn't mind *helping* usually.
Mike sometimes does *the shopping*, but that's all, really.
I have to do all *the cleaning* of course.
Paul does *the ironing* quite often — that's a great help because I hate *ironing*. And he's a very good cook. He usually does *the cooking* at weekends. We both enjoy *cooking*, in fact.
I like cooking too, but Mike's no good at it. I do *the cooking* in our house. And I do all *the washing*. Mike doesn't even know how to use the washing-machine!

94

1 They insist on going on strike.
2 He thinks it's wrong to risk starting a world war.
3 They're tired of working for low wages.
4 She doesn't agree with cutting down trees.
5 He wants the government to stop helping the Magundians.
6 They believe in talking about peace, not war.
7 She's keen on banning nuclear bombs.
8 He doesn't like being out of work.

95

He's stopped us having coffee breaks.
He's always telling us to work hard.
He doesn't agree with people working at their own speed.
He quite often wants me to work late.
I wouldn't mind him/his asking me occasionally.
He seems to expect me to spend my life at the office.
I don't like him watching me all the time.
He hates people being friendly with him.

96

1 Let her talk to the press. She likes/enjoys/loves talking to the press.
2 You'd better let them photograph her. Melinda likes/enjoys/loves being photographed.
3 Don't laugh at her. She doesn't like/She hates being laughed at.
4 Try to arrange things so that she doesn't have to wait around. Melinda doesn't like/Melinda hates waiting around/having to wait around.
5 You'll have to look after her. She likes/enjoys/loves being looked after.
6 She won't get up early. Melinda doesn't like/Melinda hates getting up early.
7 It doesn't matter if people stare at her. She likes/enjoys/loves being stared at.
8 Never ignore her. She doesn't like/She hates being ignored.

97

Milchester Council has decided *to let* 82-year-old Mrs Nellie Battle go on *living* at her home at 29 Croft Street. The Council had wanted *to knock* down all the old houses in the street because they were planning *to build* a new car park there. The future of this plan is now uncertain.

The story began five years ago when the people of Croft Street agreed *to move* to new homes. Unfortunately the Council forgot *to ask* Mrs Battle. When they finally remembered her, everyone else had already gone. But the Council failed *to persuade* Nellie to do the same. 'My grandson's just finished *decorating* the sitting-room for me,' she said at the time. 'I can't imagine *leaving* now.'

The Council offered *to pay* Mrs Battle £500 and promised *to give* her a new house, but she still refused *to move*. 'I can't help *liking* it here,' she told our reporter. 'I miss *seeing* the neighbours of course. I enjoyed *talking* to them.' Croft Street has stood almost empty for the last five years. There seemed *to be* no way anyone could move Nellie from number 29.

Now comes the Council's new decision. Mrs Battle is very pleased. 'I kept *telling* them I wouldn't move,' she said today. 'I don't mind *being* on my own any more. And I expect *to live* till I'm a hundred. I hope *to be* here a long time yet.'

We have also heard this week that the Council cannot now afford *to build* the car park. One or two of the people who used *to live* in Croft Street have suggested *repairing* the old houses so that they can move back into them. They dislike *living* in the new houses they moved into five years ago.

98

1 He heard a/the telephone ringing. It went on for a long time.
2 He saw a plane crash into the sea.
3 He saw a bird flying in the sky.
4 He heard a woman screaming. He thought she would never stop.
5 He saw a man jump out of a car as it was moving.
6 He saw a tree burning.

99

Have we done all the shopping now?
Yes, I think so. I must remember *to post* this letter.
I remember *passing* a postbox somewhere.
Just a minute, where's my purse? It isn't in my handbag. Did you forget *to bring* it?
No, I had it not long ago. And my credit card is in there. Oh, my God, what are we going to do?
Just stop *worrying* and think. You must have put it down somewhere and forgotten *to pick* it up. Try *to remember* when you had it last.
I remember *having* it in the shoe shop.

Then you stopped *to buy* a newspaper ...
Oh, it's all right. It's here in the shopping bag. Sorry. I can't remember *putting* it there.
You could try *chaining* it to your hand next time.

100

There was an earthquake in the Kitamo region at ten o'clock yesterday morning. It lasted about a minute. Many buildings collapsed. *Frightened* people ran into the streets. Many were injured by *falling* bricks and stones. After the earthquake, buildings in many parts of the city caught fire. The heat was so great that firemen could not get near many of the *burning* buildings. Hundreds of people have died. The hospital is still standing, but there aren't enough beds for all the *injured* people. Things look very bad in Kitamo now. There are hundreds of badly *damaged* houses, and those that caught fire are now just *smoking* ruins. The streets are covered with *broken* glass, and *fallen* trees block the way. Everywhere there is the sound of *crying* children.

101

1 Hurrying along the street, he suddenly stopped outside a travel agency./He hurried along the street, suddenly stopping outside a travel agency.
2 Standing outside, he looked twice at his watch./He stood outside, looking twice at his watch.
3 Having waited five minutes, he continued along Oxford Street to Hyde Park.
4 He ate a sandwich sitting on a seat.
5 Having looked again at the paper, he put it in a litter bin.
6 Leaving the park,/Having left the park, he stood at the side of the road.
7 Running into the road, he stopped a taxi.

102

1 Warned by air traffic control, the airport fire service prepared to fight a fire.
2 Believing the aircraft was going to crash, some of the passengers shouted in panic.
3 Having brought the plane down safely, the pilot felt very relieved.
4 Worried by the risk of fire, everyone hurried to get out.
5 Using chemicals, the firemen soon put out the fire.
6 Having had enough excitement for one day, most of the passengers put off their journey.

103

This small country is mostly farmland. The *animals* seen most often are *cows* and *sheep*. Most *farms* have a few *geese*, too. There are *donkeys*, but not many *horses*. There's a lot of wheat and *potatoes*, and there are *tomatoes* on the south side of the hills. In summer the *men*, *women* and *children* work together in the *fields* seven *days* a week. The *people* work hard all their *lives*.

The only two *factories* in the country are in the capital. One makes *toys* and *games*, and the other makes *knives* and *forks*. All these *things* are for export.

The east of the country is thick forest, the home of wild *ponies*, *deer* and *wolves*.

Photos of the *cliffs* along the coast show how beautiful the country is. But not many *tourists* visit it because the airport is too small for most *aircraft*.

104

1 She's going to give Alan a football.
2 She's bought Shaun a watch.
3 She's going to give a camera to Emma.
4 She's bought Nick a book.
5 She's bought some hankies for Angela.
6 She's going to give Matthew a game.
7 She's bought some perfume for Gillian.
8 She's going to give a scarf to Laura.

105

1 The farmer's dog
2 The roofs of the houses
3 The directors' room
4 The children's supper
5 The edge of the lake
6 The walker's rest
7 The side of the hill

106

two jars of marmalade, some eggs, a pineapple, five pounds of potatoes, some sugar, a packet of cornflakes, a loaf (of bread), some bananas, three tins of beans, some washing powder

107

The Clayton Clothing Company is going to build a new factory in Milchester. *This news was* announced by company chairman Mr David Clayton yesterday. Mr Clayton spent the morning in Milchester before returning to the Clayton *headquarters* at Granby.

The Clayton company *has* been in existence for 130 years and *is* famous for its 'Polymode' *goods*. The slogans 'You're never alone with a pair of Polymode *trousers*' and 'Polymode *jeans are* the *ones* for you' are well known. The company's profit last year of £2 million *was* the highest in the clothing business.

Mr Clayton will not say how *many* new *jobs* there will be, but my *information is* that there will be about 500. The *news is* very welcome because *work is* hard to find at the moment, and 2,000 unemployed people *is* a high figure for a small town.

Key

108

Cleopatra was an Egyptian queen.
Confucius was a Chinese philosopher.
Nehru was an Indian politician.
Newton was an English scientist.
Raphael was an Italian painter.
Rockefeller was an American industrialist.
Tolstoy was a Russian writer.
Wagner was a German composer.

109

Push *a metal rod* through *a cork* and then put two pins into *the cork*, as in Picture 1. Take two more corks and push *some nails* into them. Put *the pins* on two glasses and move *the cork* to *the right place* so that it balances, as in Picture 2. Then you need *a candle* and *some matches*. Stand *the candle* on *a saucer* under one side of *the rod* and light it. *The heat* that comes from *the candle* will make *the metal* expand (= grow bigger). This extra length will make *the rod* fall, as in Picture 3. *The experiment* shows that *heat* makes *metal* expand.

110

Thomas French was one of the greatest explorers in *history*. He travelled to *South America, Greenland* and many other parts of *the world*. He was born in *1886*, on *Christmas Day*. His family lived near *Regent's Park*. They were rich, and *money* was never a problem. Thomas left *school* because he wanted to go to *sea*. He sailed across *the Atlantic Ocean* with some friends. At twenty he joined an expedition to *Africa*. Later he led expeditions to *the Andes*, to both Poles and even to parts of *the USSR*. He also climbed *Mount Everest* twice. *The history* of all these journeys is in his diaries, which show us *the life* of an explorer in the 1920's. *Breakfast* was French's favourite meal, and he always ate well. He went to *bed* early but often got up in *the night* to write his diary. He also took hundreds of photos, which are now on show at *the National Gallery*.

111

Graham Mackay is *an* engineer. He works on *an* oil rig in *the* North Sea. He works on *the* rig for two weeks and then has two weeks *at home* in Glasgow. *The* rig is 100 miles off *the* coast of Scotland. *The* oil company's helicopter flies him to and *from* Aberdeen Airport. He does *an* important job, and he's paid over £350 *a* week.

Graham works twelve hours *a* day during his two weeks on *the* rig. His shift finishes *at midnight*, when he goes *to bed*. Although *the* work is important, it's rather *a* boring job. He shares *a* cabin with three other men. One of them is *a* friend of his, *an* American called Lee Driver, who comes *from New Mexico*.

The men aren't allowed to *drink alcohol*, so Graham *has milk or tea* with his meals. Most of the men *smoke cigarettes*. *The* weather can be pretty bad. Sometimes *there are storms*. Everyone's always glad to get back to *the* mainland.

112

Trevor says we're giving a party on Saturday.
We're thinking of giving *one*. *It* was Alison who first thought of the idea.
Gary won't be here. *He*'s going to London.
Gary won't mind if we go ahead without *him*.
Are we going to have food?
It would be expensive to buy food for all the guests. Let's just ask *them* to bring something to drink.
Have we got any glasses?
There are *some* in the kitchen cupboard. *They*'ll be all right. We can use *them*.
There won't be enough, but we can borrow *some*.
We can't use my record player. There's something wrong with *it*.
What about a cassette recorder? Hasn't Daniel got *one*?
He had *one*, but he's sold *it*.
Who are we going to invite?
Who was that girl who came here on Friday?
Rosemary.
Well, don't invite *her*. *She* wasn't very nice. I don't like *her* at all.
We all went to Margaret and Angela's party, so we ought to invite *them*. But let's talk about it tomorrow. I'm too tired tonight. *It*'s getting late.

113

1 This is Adam's ruler. It must be *his* because it's got *his* name on it.
I'll give it to *him*.
2 Are these gloves *yours*, Rebecca?
Yes, they are. Thanks. They haven't got *my* name in them, but they belong to *me*.
3 I think these notes belong to Lisa and Melanie. These pages are part of a project of *theirs*.
I can't see *their* names on it, but I'll ask *them* about it.
4 Adam and I have been looking for these magazines. Someone took them from *our* room. They belong to *us*. We're using the pictures for a project of *ours*.
5 Isn't this pen Emma's?
I don't think it's one of *hers*. I know she's lost *her* calculator, but I haven't heard *her* say she's lost a pen.
6 Is that book *mine*?
Yes, it's got *your* name in it, so it must belong to *you*. Here you are.
Thanks, Gary.

114

I go to Weight Losers now, you know. I'm trying to lose weight. I have to force *myself* to eat the right food. My husband doesn't think I'm fat. 'You'll make *yourself* ill,' he tells me. But it's doing me good. Lots of people go to the club. They're all trying to lose weight or keep *themselves* slim. We all weigh *ourselves* on the scales and write down our weight. Then the members all tell *each other* their weight. Yesterday one man was one kilo heavier than the week before. He said he couldn't stop *himself* eating cakes. The teacher says 'You must control *yourselves*, all of you!' Helen goes too, you know. She's losing weight. She's very pleased with *herself*. The Johnsons were there yesterday too. They're always arguing with *each other*. They've lost a lot of weight, so they must be really starving *themselves*.

115

Lots of people have already bought Bill Hawk's super new book. They've saved *themselves* a lot of money by doing jobs *themselves*. Here are a few examples.

Mr Purlin of Hamleigh repaired the roof of his house *himself*. 'We decorated the whole house *ourselves*. This book made it easy,' say the Cleat family of Huxton.
The Spriggs of Granby put in central heating *themselves*. 'I asked *myself*: why not?' said Mr Sprigg. 'With Bill Hawk's help it wasn't very difficult.'
'I put in a new bath *myself*,' says Mr Hunter of Milchester.
Mrs Flashing of Wayford says 'We wanted a garage. A friend said 'Why don't you build it *yourselves*?' He showed us the book. So we did it *ourselves*. Now we feel really pleased with *ourselves*.'
Mrs Stiles of Backworth fitted a new front door all by *herself*. 'I couldn't imagine *myself* doing anything like that until I read this book.'

116

I need a new umbrella. I really must buy *one* soon.
I saw *some nice ones* in Bymore's when I was here last month.
I don't know the stores here very well. *Which one* is Bymore's?
It's *the new one*, *the one* opposite Harridge's.
Oh, yes, I know. Actually, Diane, I think your umbrella is *a very nice one*. Where did you get it?
Oh, I've had *this one* for a long time. I don't think you'll find *one* like this now.
They must have umbrellas in this store. I wonder which floor they're on.
I think it's *this one*. Oh, yes, here they are.
I don't like *these brown ones*.
This one here is nice.

Well, I prefer *that one* next to it, *the red one*. But it's rather big. I like *the ones* that fold up very small.
There's *one* here like that.
Yes, but I don't want *one* that colour.
Which one do you like best?
I think *the ones* in Bymore's were better. Shall we go there?
Yes, OK. Which way is the escalator?
I think there's *one* over there.

117

There aren't any beds.
There are some electric cookers.
There aren't any tables.
There are some sofas.

There aren't any shelves.
There are some mirrors.
There's some wallpaper.
There isn't any paint.

118

All the luggage goes in the back. Put *everything* in the back of the bus. And *each* piece of luggage must have the owner's name on it.
I've got *something* to eat here, look.
Yes, you can keep that with you.
Is it true we'll have to do written work *every/each* evening?
Yes, it is.
I can't find a seat. There's *nowhere* for me to sit.
Well, *each* seat has a number. Yours is ten.
Neil is sitting there. He says we can have *any* seat we like.
Well, he's wrong. He'll have to sit *somewhere* else.
I think we're ready now. There's *nothing* else to do before we go.
There's *someone/somebody* missing. Nick isn't here. We've looked *everywhere* for him, but we can't find him *anywhere*. Has *anyone/anybody* seen Nick?
I've asked the others, but *no one/nobody* knows *anything* about him.
Oh, it's all right. Here he is.
I hope *everyone/everybody* has been to the toilet. We don't want to stop *every* five minutes, do we?

119

They haven't sold many machines.
They've sold a lot of steel.
They haven't sold much coal.
They haven't sold many electrical goods.
They've sold a lot of clothes.
They haven't sold much food.

They've sold fewer/less machines.
They've sold more steel.
They've sold less coal.
They've sold more electrical goods.
They've sold fewer/less clothes.
They've sold less food.

120

George Wright and his party have made far *too many* mistakes during their time as the government. Mr Wright doesn't really spend *enough* time at his job, I'm afraid. Our Prime Minister spends *too much* time playing golf. While he's doing that, our industry is dying. A lot of factories have closed in the last few years — *too many* factories, in my opinion. And we've just learnt that *some more* factories are going to close soon, thanks to George Wright again. The Progressives simply don't spend *enough* money on the really important things, like helping industry. And of course they spend *too much* on things that no one needs. We don't want *another* Progressive government after this one. Mr Wright would like to give us *some more* of the same medicine. But the medicine is killing our country. You gave the Progressives a chance to put the country right, and you've seen the result. Don't give them *another* chance.

121

1 One of them is an island.
2 Neither of them is/are in Spain.
3 Three of them are in South America.
4 Both of them are oceans.
5 Two of them are in London.
6 All of them are in the USA.
7 None of them is/are in Europe.
8 Both of them are in Australia.

122

1 *What's* your name?
2 *Where* do you live?
3 And *whose* is the bicycle? *Who* owns it?
4 *When* was it stolen?
5 *Where* did you leave it?
6 *What time* was this?
7 *What kind* of bicycle is it?
8 *What colour* is it?
9 *How old* is it?
10 *How much* did it cost?

123

1 (And) who loves Princess Flora? ~ Mike Perry.
2 (And) who does Princess Flora love? ~ Lord Midwinter.
3 (And) who does Peter Kane love? ~ Sophie Salinsky.
4 (And) who does Lord Midwinter love? ~ Sophie Salinsky.
5 (And) who loves Lord Midwinter? ~ Princess Flora.
6 (And) who loves Sophie Salinsky? ~ Lord Midwinter and Peter Kane.
7 (And) who does Sophie Salinsky love? ~ Mike Perry.
8 (And) who does Jackie Logan love? ~ Mike Perry.

124

1 *What* goes up but never comes down?
2 *Who* is paid money for taking something away from you?
3 *What* can go through a closed door?
4 *Which* of these words is longer: 'laughs' or 'smiles'?
5 *What* has fingers but no arms?
6 *Which* sheep eat more grass, black ones or white ones?
7 *Who* invented the first pen?
8 *Which* has more tails, one cat or no cat?
9 *What* is the difference between an African elephant and an Indian elephant?
10 *Which* king of England wore the biggest shoes?

125

I was waiting for someone.
Who were you waiting for?
I don't know. I was afraid of something.
What were you afraid of?
I'm not sure. Somebody ran towards me.
Who ran towards you?
A man I didn't know. Then I shouted at someone.
Who did you shout at?
I think it was my brother. But then I fell over something.
What did you fall over?
Something lying in the road. Somebody was pointing at me.
Who was pointing at you?
My father. He was talking to someone.
Who was he talking to?
I don't know. I woke up then.

126

1 'The Mind Machine' is about a computer which controls people's thoughts.
2 'Eureka!' is about a scientist who discovers the secret of the universe.
3 'Spaceville' is about some people who build a city in space.
4 'Zero' is about an accident which starts a nuclear war.
5 'The President' is about a dictator who rules the world.
6 'Danger Hour' is about a cloud of gas which pollutes the earth.
7 'Starfight' is about a war which breaks out in space.
8 'Wait for Death' is about a man who lives for a thousand years.

127

1 Socks are things (that/which) you wear on your feet.
2 A briefcase is something (that/which) you carry papers in.
3 A greengrocer is someone who sells fruit and vegetables.
4 A present is something (that/which) you give to someone.
5 A kettle is something (that/which) heats water.
6 Soap is something (that/which) you wash with.
7 A target is something (that/which) you try to hit.

8 An artist is someone who paints pictures.
9 A seat is something (that/which) you sit on.
10 An umbrella is something (that/which) keeps the rain off you.
11 Oars are things (that/which) you use to row a boat.
12 A mirror is something (that/which) you can see yourself in.

128

1 Those are the friends I went with.
2 That's the pool we swam in.
3 That's the dress I bought.
4 Those are the people/some people we met.
5 That's the boat we went for a sail in.
6 That's the castle we visited.
7 That's the beach we liked.
8 That's the lake we walked round.

129

I saw Roger Cowley on Saturday.
Roger Cowley?
Yes, he's the man *who works at Electrobrit.*
It's Roger Cowley *whose wife owns the Top Shop.*
What's the Top Shop?
It's the shop *that/which sells dresses.* It's the one
(*that/which*) *I went in yesterday.*
Oh, I know. It was Roger Cowley *whose car was stolen from
outside his house.*
That's right. It was the car (*that/which*) *he bought from
Richard Hunter.*
And who's Richard Hunter?
I don't think you've met him. He's the man (*who*) *I invited to
our party.* He didn't come, though.
Is he the man *whose sister was on a TV quiz show*?
No, that's Bob. Richard is the man (*who*) *David plays golf
with.*
Yes, but I was talking about Roger Cowley.

130

1 Food bought at Brisco costs you less.
2 Someone listening to a Meditone radio hears every word.
3 Cakes made with Bakewell flour taste wonderful.
4 Hed-Cure is the only thing to make your headache really
better.
5 A person sitting in a Super-Plush chair is sitting comfortably.
6 The most exciting toy to give your child is a Playworld toy.
7 Everyone notices the man wearing a Windsor shirt.
8 A floor covered with a Wonderlay carpet looks ten times
better.

131

1 Len, who has finally found a new job, is giving a big party.
2 Craig, who/whom Len has invited, is hoping that Donna will
be at the party.

3 Craig also wants to borrow some money from Gordon,
whose cycle repair business is doing very well.
4 The new club in Jubilee Road, which everyone is talking
about, is very popular with young people.
5 A disco, which took place at the club last weekend, kept
people awake half the night.
6 The new manager at the plastics factory, who/whom no one
likes, wants Donna to work late.
7 He has arranged a staff meeting, which starts at ten o'clock
tomorrow.
8 Donna is staying at number 33 with Teresa, who has given
her the spare room.
9 The woman at number 35, who Donna spoke to yesterday,/
to whom Donna spoke yesterday, is behaving rather
strangely.
10 Meanwhile Robin, whose wife has left him, is explaining his
problems to Harriet.

132

1 The Superior is just as comfortable as the Libretto.
2 The Swift is more spacious than the Sahara.
3 The Delta is cheaper than the Prince.
4 The Sahara is just as reliable as the Libretto.
5 The Prince is less comfortable than the Swift./The Prince
isn't as comfortable as the Swift.
6 The Delta is faster than the Sahara.
7 The Superior is less economical than the Delta./The Superior
isn't as economical as the Delta.
8 The Swift is easier to drive than the Superior.
9 The Sahara is better-looking than the Prince.
10 The Swift is more comfortable than the Libretto.
11 The Prince is the most reliable.
12 The Swift is the easiest to drive.
13 The Swift is the most comfortable.
14 The Libretto is the most spacious.
15 The Superior is the fastest.
16 The Superior is the best-looking.

133

I think we should go. You'll get a *higher* salary with Multitech
than you do now, and we'll have a *better* standard of living.
Don't forget London is the *most expensive* place we could
possibly go to. For example, house prices are the *highest* in
the country. A house will be *more difficult* to find there than in
Milchester.
But it's probably the *biggest* chance you'll ever get. That's
the *most important* thing. And it'll be *easier* for me to find a
good job than it was here.
London is a *bigger* place than Milchester. Life won't be so
quiet.
Well, I'd like a *more exciting* life. It is a bit boring here
sometimes. And it'll be much *more convenient* for shops and
theatres, living in London. You've never really liked your job

here. And things have got *worse* recently.
Yes, they have. And Multitech is certainly one of the *best* companies in the business. But I don't want to go unless you really want to.

134

1 Food is getting more and more expensive. The more expensive it becomes, the hungrier/the more hungry people are.
2 Industry is getting weaker and weaker. The weaker it becomes, the greater our problems are.
3 Things are getting worse and worse. The worse they become, the more important it is to do something.
4 People are getting poorer and poorer. The poorer they become, the smaller our chances of success are.
5 The situation is getting more and more hopeless. The more hopeless it becomes, the more difficult it is to put (it) right.
6 People are getting more and more desperate. The more desperate they become, the more necessary it is to act.

135

Dear Helen,

Thank you for your letter. Is it *really* four months since I last wrote? I'm sorry, but I've been very busy *lately*.

I'm *already* working for my exams./I'm working for my exams *already*. I've planned my revision *carefully*./I've *carefully* planned my revision. I *usually* work/*Usually* I work until about ten o'clock in the evening./I work until about ten o'clock in the evening *usually*. I've *just* finished for today.

Of course I don't *always* keep to my plan./I don't *always* keep to my plan *of course*. I saw a marvellous film *yesterday*./*Yesterday* I saw a marvellous film. It was called 'The Secret Game'. Have you seen it?
Actually I don't *often* go out./I don't go out *often, actually*. Suzanne comes *here* about once a week. We talk *a lot*.

I hope to visit England again *next year*./*Next year* I hope to visit England again. I had a lovely time *there* last year. It would be great to see you *again*. I'm trying *hard* to save some money.

How are you? Is your new flat all right? Please write *soon*.

Love,

Maria

136

1 Stella is progressing satisfactorily. She does her homework well.
2 Emil speaks English fluently. He reads widely.
3 Milena works hard. She learns fast.
4 Victor speaks slowly. He pronounces some common words incorrectly.

137

1 The service at the Grand is fairly good. It's a bit less good than at the Castle. The service at the Castle is very good.
2 The food at the Grand isn't very good. It's a lot less good than at the Castle. The food at the Castle is very good.
3 The Grand is very clean. It's a lot cleaner than the Castle. The Castle isn't very clean.
4 The Grand is fairly quiet. It's a bit less quiet than the Castle. The Castle is very quiet.
5 The Grand is very convenient. It's a bit more convenient than the Castle. The Castle is fairly convenient.
6 The prices at the Grand aren't very reasonable. They're a lot less reasonable than at the Castle. The prices at the Castle are very reasonable.

138

She doesn't often argue with people.
She often worries.
She never takes risks.
She's always late for work.
She doesn't often tell jokes.
She usually laughs at comedy shows.
She often wishes things were different.
She isn't often sad.

139

Well, the party is going very *nicely*, isn't it? Have one of these sausages. They taste *good*.
No, thanks.
You don't sound very *happy*, Angela. And you look *pale*. Are you all right?
I feel rather *tired*. And I'm *hot*.
It is getting a bit *warm* in here, isn't it? Well, I can *easily* open this window.
Thanks. Actually, my head aches quite *badly* too. I think it's *slowly* getting worse.
I'm *sure* the music isn't helping. It seems rather *loud*, doesn't it? Look, would you like me to take you home?
No, it's all right, thanks. But if I could sit *quietly* somewhere for a few minutes, I might be OK.
I'll ask Lynn if there's somewhere you can go.

140

1 You have to speak really clearly. Can you speak *more clearly*, please, Helen?
2 You didn't wait long enough, Lynn. Can you stay a little *longer* in the doorway?
3 You haven't learnt your words very well, Peter. I hope you know them *better* next time.
4 You aren't angry enough, Sarah. Can you shout rather *more angrily*?
5 Angela, that isn't far enough. Walk *further/farther* to the left.

6 And you're supposed to be nervous. Can you look round a bit *more nervously*?
7 I want you to hit the table hard. You can hit it *harder* than that, Bob.
8 Be careful when you lay the table, Sue. Try to do it *more carefully* next time.

141

Street scene. There are three shops. *In* the middle there is a baker's, which is *between* an antique shop and a toy shop. The toy shop is *on* the right. There is a phone box *on* the left *at/on* the corner of the street. A car is coming *round* the corner. There is a man on a bike *behind* the car. There is also a car parked *opposite* the baker's. This car has a suitcase *on* its roof. A woman is just stepping *off* the pavement to walk *across* the road. She has come *from* the baker's/*out of* the baker's. Two girls are standing *outside/by/ near* the baker's. A window cleaner is climbing *up* a ladder *to/towards* the window *above* the toy shop. He has got a bucket *in* his hand. A woman is looking *out of* the window/ *through* the window. A boy is walking *along/on* the pavement *under* the ladder *towards* the street corner. There is a man *in/inside* the antique shop looking *through* an old telescope. There is a young man *in/inside* the phone box, and three people are standing *on* the pavement waiting — a woman, a man and a boy. The boy is *at* the back of the queue.

142

Stan Crowe hopes to run against James Boto of Kenya in a 1500 metres race in Paris *on* June 16th. Both men will want to break Cliff Holding's world record. Holding ran the 1500 metres *in* 3 minutes 28 seconds last year. Holding will also be running in Seattle *on* June 14th, two days *before* the Paris meeting.

British fans have been hoping *for* several months to see Crowe win back his record. He last ran against Boto *in* April, when he fell and hurt himself *during* the race. He was just behind Boto *at* the time. The two men had not met *since* the last Olympic games in Peking. Crowe has had to rest *after/ since* his accident, but he was back in action *at* seven o'clock *on* Saturday evening when he won a rather slow race in Edinburgh. He hopes to be fully fit *by* the end of this month at the latest. If he is not fit for Paris, he will have to wait *until/till* the Commonwealth Games. These games take place in Ottawa *from* August 14th *to/until/till* the 20th.

143

On a Thursday evening *in* October, 1931, *at* about eight o'clock, the ship 'Voyager' sank. The ship had been sailing *since* the end of September, when she left London, and was on her way *from* England *to* Australia. The only survivor was an Englishman called Wilfred Batty, who saved himself *by*

swimming two miles. He spent three years *on* an island *in* the middle of the Indian Ocean.

The island was quite small, and he could walk *round* the whole of it *in* an hour. He climbed *up* the one hill and put a flag *on* it *as* a signal. *At* night Batty slept *in* a cave, where he felt quite *at* home. *During/In* the day, he often fished *with* a home-made net. He cooked the fish *over/on* a wood fire.

Batty stayed *on* the island *for* almost three years, *until/till* August 1934. A ship was sailing *past/near* the island, and the captain saw Batty's signal. The sailors found a man *in* a long blue coat *with* dark hair and a beard, looking rather *like* a gorilla. Batty was soon home, and a few years later he finally arrived in Australia *by* air.

144

1 Prices will rise. The question is, how <u>much</u> will they go up?
2 Someone calculated these figures, but the government won't say <u>who</u> worked them out.
3 The Prime Minister says he's going to raise the question in Brussels, but <u>when</u> is he going to bring it up?
4 We know the petrol tank exploded. <u>Why</u> did it blow up?
5 So the government are going to increase taxes. Well, how <u>much</u> are they going to put them up?
6 The Council say they're going to demolish the building, but <u>why</u> are they going to knock it down?
7 The government say they discovered the mistake, but <u>when</u> did they find it out?
8 The plan succeeded. <u>Why</u> did it come off?

145

1 We didn't close them down.
2 We didn't put it up.
3 But we listened to them.
4 We didn't let it down.
5 But we didn't have to look for them/look for any.
6 We dealt with it.
7 We kept it down.
8 But we care about them.

146

1 It is important to act quickly. *As soon as* you see a customer behaving suspiciously, inform the control team by radio.
2 Follow the customer *as* he moves around the store.
3 Do not speak to the customer inside the store. Wait *until* he has left the store.
4 *After* you have informed the control team, a second detective will join you to help with the arrest.
5 Arrest the customer outside and bring him to the control room for questioning. Do not question him *before* you get to the control room.
6 Remember that the control team have been filming the customer *since* you first informed them about him.

Key

147

1 I've no idea what my name is.
2 I don't know where I live.
3 I've got a feeling (that) I'm a long way from home.
4 I'm not sure why I think so.
5 I know (that) something strange has happened to me.
6 I can't understand how it happened.
7 I've heard (that) I just walked into the hospital.
8 I can't remember when I came here.

148

1 Ingrid is learning it because she likes learning languages.
2 Anita is learning it so that she can help her daughter with her homework.
3 Martin is learning it because he might need it some time.
4 Claudia is learning it (because she wants) to get a better job.
5 Gaston is learning it so that he'll be able to understand/so that he can understand American films better.
6 Andrea is learning it because she has to do it at school.
7 Sven is learning it so that he'll be able to read/so that he can read engineering textbooks in English.
8 Jan is learning it (because he wants) to impress his girl-friend.

149

1 There was fog, so their flight was delayed.
2 The plane was so late (that) they got to bed at three in the morning.
3 It was such a long way to the beach (that) it took an hour from the hotel.
4 It was such a crowded beach (that) there was hardly room to sit down.
5 The hotel was so noisy (that) they couldn't sleep.
6 Their room had such an unpleasant view (that) it made them feel quite miserable.
7 They weren't enjoying themselves, so they went home.
8 The holiday was so disappointing (that) they decided to ask for their money back.

150

Driving a car can be expensive. The bicycle, *on the other hand*, is a cheap form of transport. A bicycle *not only* costs very little *but also* lasts much longer than a car. It is *also* very cheap to use *because* of course it doesn't need any fuel. In fact, it costs practically nothing *after* you've bought it. It *also* helps keep you fit *because* you get exercise *when* you ride it. Another good thing about a bicycle is *that* it doesn't pollute the air. *If* everyone rode bicycles instead of driving cars, we wouldn't be using up the world's oil so quickly.

Although the bicycle has these advantages, it has some disadvantages too. It is convenient only for relatively short journeys, *whereas* by car you can travel quite a long way in comfort. Another problem is *that* the cyclist is not protected from the weather and gets wet *when/if* it rains. Cycling isn't very nice in heavy traffic *either*. In Britain there are very few cycle paths, *so* bicycles have to share the road with cars and lorries. The best place for a bike ride is a quiet country lane. Main roads and city streets are often *so* busy *that* it needs some courage to take a bike on them. The cyclist has no protection, and *so* he is more likely than a motorist to be seriously hurt *or* killed *if* he does have an accident. Cycling keeps you healthy, *but* the cars may kill you!

151

The car doesn't feel safe.
It *does feel safe*. There's nothing wrong with it.
The lights don't work.
They do work. We mended them.
You didn't replace the front tyres.
We did replace them. I remember doing it.
The back doors won't open.
They will open, you know.
And the heater doesn't work.
It does work. We checked it.
But you didn't check the battery.
Yes, *we did check it*. The battery is OK.
Anyway, the bill isn't correct.
It is correct. I wrote it myself.
You don't know what you're talking about.
We do know/I do know what we're/I'm talking about.
Repairing cars is our business.

152

1 It was Bozo who shot the policeman in Marseilles.
2 It was in Monaco that he went into hiding.
3 It was Ross who bought the guns.
4 It's the Standard Bank that they're planning to rob next.
5 It's Gregory who finds out all the inside information.
6 It's on Long Island that they're going to meet next week.
7 It's Morocco that Grabski intends to go to afterwards.
8 It's the Mafia that/who he's afraid of.

153

1 It was the Atlas that/which won the 'Road' magazine prize.
2 It did win the Monte Carlo rally last year.
3 What the Atlas gives you is reliability.
4 You do have lots of room in an Atlas.
5 It's the expert design that/which makes you feel so comfortable.
6 What you'll never believe is how much luggage it holds.
7 It's the low price that/which will really surprise you.
8 The Atlas does cost less than £7,000.
9 What you'll never want to do is let anyone else drive your Atlas.
10 What you ought to be driving now is an Atlas.